KEY STAGE

C000138546

English

KS2 SAT Practice Papers

Instructions, Guidance, Practice Papers & Answers

CONTENTS

how2become

As part of this product you have also received FREE access to online tests that will help you to pass Key Stage 2 ENGLISH
(SATs Practice Papers).

To gain access, simply go to:

www.PsychometricTestsOnline.co.uk

Get more products
for passing any test at:

www.How2Become.com

Orders: Please contact How2Become Ltd, Suite 14, 50 Churchill Square Business Centre, Kings Hill, Kent ME19 4YU.

You can order through Amazon.co.uk under ISBN 9781910602874, via the website www.How2Become.com or through Gardners.com.

ISBN: 9781910602874

First published in 2016 by How2Become Ltd.

Copyright © 2016 How2Become.

Typeset for How2Become Ltd by Anton Pshinka.

Disclaimer

Every effort has been made to ensure that the information contained within this guide is accurate at the time of publication. How2Become Ltd is not responsible for anyone failing any part of any selection process as a result of the information contained within this guide. How2Become Ltd and their authors cannot accept any responsibility for any errors or omissions within this guide, however caused. No responsibility for loss or damage occasioned by any person acting, or refraining from action, as a result of the material in this publication can be accepted by How2Become Ltd.

The information within this guide does not represent the views of any third party service or organisation.

Using your papers

Read the **instructions** carefully before working through your practice papers.

*In this book, there are **two** sets of practice papers:*

Set A and **Set B**

Each **set** includes:

Paper 1 – Questions

45 minutes   **Marks out of 50**

Paper 2 – Spelling

15 minutes   **Marks out of 20**

Paper 3 – Reading

1 hour   **Marks out of 50**

Before working through the practice papers, make sure that you have the following:

- The correct testing paper;
- A blue or black pen/dark pencil;
- Rubber (optional).

How to answer the questions:

Some of the questions in the practice papers will provide you with just an answer box, which you will need to fill in with your answer.

Be sure that your answer is **clear**.

If you write the wrong answer and wish to change it, neatly draw a cross through the incorrect answer, and write the correct answer. Make sure your answer is still written in the answer box.

| ~~Wrong answer~~ | New answer |

Some questions will require longer answers. This is indicated in two ways:

1. The number of marks the question is worth;
2. How many lines are provided for your answer.

The above indicates an answer that requires more detail.

The above line indicates an answer that requires few words or a simple sentence.

REMEMBER – the key thing to look out for is how many marks each question is worth. The number of marks for each question is written on the right side of each testing page.

2 marks

Time management:

It is important that you **know the duration** of each testing paper.

Be sure to **read the front of your practice papers CAREFULLY.** This will tell you the duration of each practice paper. You can use this time limit to your advantage by estimating how long you should be spending on each question.

If you do not know the answer to one of the questions, **leave it**, and **come back** to it at the end if you have time.

If you finish before the end, go back through the paper and **check your work**.

Make sure your answers are written **clearly**.

Cross out any incorrect answers or anything that you do not want to be marked.

Guidance for parents

Welcome to your child's Key Stage 2 English Practice Papers!

How to mark your child's paper:

To determine how well your child is performing in their practice papers, use the answers at the end of each **set** to mark each practice paper. For Papers 1, 2 and 3 of each set, the score will be **out of 120**.

The below tables demonstrate how you should mark your child's test papers. At the end of each set, you will be given a chance to mark the papers using the answers provided.

	Paper 1 Mark out of 50	**Paper 2** Mark out of 20	**Paper 3** Mark out of 50	**TOTAL** Mark out of 120
SET A				

	Paper 1 Mark out of 50	**Paper 2** Mark out of 20	**Paper 3** Mark out of 50	**TOTAL** Mark out of 120
SET B				

Please note that the total marks for our practice papers DO NOT reflect the actual total marks for the real testing papers. Instead, these should be used as a way of monitoring how well your child is progressing at home.

How to monitor your child's progression:

➤ The optimum way to monitor your child's progression before their English examinations, is to use practice papers to assess how much your child is improving.

➤ Although you do not want to bombard your child with testing papers, giving your child a few practice papers leading up to their SATs will allow them to progress at a steady speed.

➤ Instead of cramming in loads of practice a couple of weeks before your child's exam, you should try spreading these out across a few months. That way, your child will feel more relaxed, which will improve their learning over longer periods of time.

➤ Ultimately, the more practice that your child endures, the better results they will achieve in their SATs.

➤ We strongly advise that you work through a practice paper with your child, to find out what they struggle with. You can then work on those weaker areas to ensure they are bettered. You can test their progression by giving your child the same questions to practice with, and see whether they have learnt how to work them out. If they have, then move on to the next weak area. If not, continue working on those questions until they master them. Do this for each of their weak areas, until they feel fully competent in tackling all the questions.

How to help your child succeed:

➤ Encourage your child to be confident in their abilities. Show them that you are proud of them.

➤ Make sure your child is getting enough sleep.

➤ Make sure they are eating balanced meals, especially for breakfast.

- Sit with them whilst they complete their revision books. This will show a great level of support.

- Encourage them to ask for help at school if they are struggling with anything.

- Set aside pre-planned time for revision.

- When going through their revision booklets, make sure that your child is referring back to the text; they can gain extra marks for using direct examples from the text.

- Make sure that your child has everything they need for their revision (i.e. pens, paper, revision guides, etc.).

- Be relaxed. When your child comes home from school, ensure that their home environment is relaxed. This will reduce the pressure your child may be feeling.

- After your child has spent some time revising, reward them with free time/ play time. This will boost their energy levels and allow them to continue with their normal routine.

- Allow for plenty of study breaks – even if they're 5 or 10 minutes long. This will help to refresh the memory and keep your child calm and focused.

- **KEEP IN MIND** – a child's attention span is usually between 30 to 50 minutes.

- Active revision is a great way to stay interactive with the topic. Revision games and mock tests are great exam techniques to use to prepare for the exams.

- Visual aids are another great way to take in lots of information. Mind maps, spider diagrams, flash cards and posters should all be used in preparation.

- Brush up on your vocabulary. These types of tests are designed to assess your English and vocabulary skills. Therefore you need to be able to demonstrate a strong level of ability regarding words, phrases and meanings.

- We have also created other Key Stage 2 English books which provide further practice for English SATs. This guarantees that your child will be fully prepared for *every* type of question.

For more information on our Key Stage 2 books, please visit our website

www.how2become.com

or go on to

www.amazon.co.uk

and search 'Key Stage 2 English is Easy'

KEY STAGE 2 English

SET A
Practice Paper 1
Grammar, Punctuation & Spelling

Questions

45 minutes

First Name	
Middle Name/s	
Last Name	
School	
Date of Birth	*D D / M M / Y Y Y Y*

1 Lalita needs your help! Draw a line to match each **prefix** with the correct word, in order to make a new word.

PREFIX

WORD

DIS

IN

COM

RE

MIS

CITE

LEAD

APPEAR

ACTIVE

MOTION

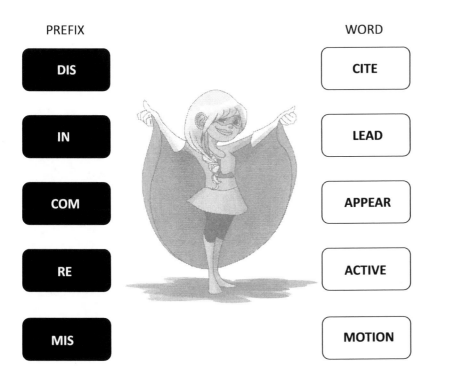

1 mark

 2 Circle the **correct spelling** of the word in the sentences below.

a) I am quiet / quite happy with my exam results.

b) We need to alter this loose / lose knot.

c) Are / Our shopping trip was really successful.

d) My grandpa is really fragile and week / weak.

e) The you / yew / ewe gave birth to a lamb.

1 mark

3 Write the **contracted form** of the words underlined in the sentences below.

I think <u>I have</u> forgotten where our car is parked. I <u>cannot</u> see it.

[   ]

[   ]

We <u>are not</u> allowed to go beyond this point. <u>We will</u> be in really big trouble.

[   ]

[   ]

4 Tick the box to show whether the highlighted word is a **verb, adverb** or **adjective.**

SENTENCE	VERB	ADVERB	ADJECTIVE
The **hairy** man who sat in the corner.			
I **accepted** the consequences.			
I had to **identify** an unusual insect.			
The duck **gracefully** swam across the pond.			
I **always** check over my homework.			
My friend was **questioned** by the police.			

2 marks

5 Preston needs your help! He wants you to underline ALL of the **adjectives** in the sentences below.

1. Andy was a spontaneous man. He was confident and enthusiastic and liked to seek adventures.

2. The courageous 90 year old woman was praised for her bravery.

3. The thunderstorm sounded angry and violent.

4. It was a cunning plan, and no one would be any the wiser.

1 mark

6 What does struct mean in the below words? Tick **one**.

in<u>struct</u>   recon<u>struct</u>   in<u>struct</u>or

Collide ☐

Dismantle ☐

Build ☐

Generate ☐

Hold ☐

1 mark

7 Which sentences are punctuated correctly? Tick **two**.

"Is it dinner time yet?" shouted Elizabeth, who was eager to eat. ☐

It was a cold thundery night. ☐

Ryan asked whether it was time for bed? ☐

The jury finally reached a verdict – not guilty. ☐

My mothers friend brought me some flowers, they were beautiful. ☐

☐ 1 mark

8 Insert a **pair of brackets** in the correct place, in order to make the sentence read correctly.

Harrison Blake Chairman of the Football Committee has decided to resign after 6 years.

☐ 1 mark

9 Complete the sentence using a **possessive pronoun**.

This necklace is _ .

☐ 1 mark

10 Rewrite the following sentences so that each sentence contains a **possessive apostrophe**.

a) The tail that belongs to the cat.

_____

_____

b) Ryan has shoes that are old and dirty.

_____

_____

c) The prams that belonged to the women.

_____

_____

1 mark

11 Insert a **semi-colon** in the correct place in the sentence below.

Come back at the end of the day I will have made a decision.

1 mark

12 Complete each sentence by circling the correct **pronoun**.

1. Can _____ all listen to the following instructions?
(you,   I,   our)

2. It wasn't _____ to give away. (their,   theirs,   her)

3. It was _____ decision. (him,   his,   he)

4. The car was at the garage because _____ needed fixing. (them,   it)

1 mark

17

13 Use the table below, and write the adjectives in both their **comparative form** and **superlative form.**

ADJECTIVE	COMPARATIVE	SUPERLATIVE
Bright		
Fine		
Funny		
Brave		
Friendly		
Beautiful		

1 mark

14 Explain how the **commas** change the meaning of both sentences below:

Mountain gorillas, which live in Africa, are endangered animals.

Mountain gorillas which live in Africa are endangered animals.

_____

_____

_____

_____

_____

_____

1 mark

15 Freddie needs your help! For the following sentences, write two **synonyms** for the highlighted words.

a) I felt so **comfortable**.

_____

_____

b) It should have been **obvious**.

_____

_____

c) There was a **peculiar** sound.

_____

_____

1 mark

16 Anil needs your help! For the following sentences, write two **antonyms** for the highlighted words.

a) It was absolutely **certain**.

_____

_____

b) I was unbelievably **happy**.

_____

_____

c) It was a **fact**.

_____

_____

1 mark

17 Tick the box to say whether the bold statement is a **main clause** or **subordinate clause**.

Sentence	Main Clause	Subordinate Clause
Polly, **a year younger than me**, had to stay at home.		
Mr Smith, **who was Head of PE**, is leaving.		
After she picks me up, **my sister is taking me to get some ice cream**.		
Although I was scared, **I walked into the room**.		

1 mark

18 Rewrite the following sentences, changing the **passive voice** into **active voice**.

a) The cereal box had been knocked over by Daniel.

....

....

b) The ball was kicked over the fence by Sam.

....

....

c) The windows were washed by the boy.

....

....

1 mark

20

19 Rewrite the following sentences, changing the **active voice** into **passive voice**.

a) Gina told Ella a secret.

_____

_____

b) A child pushed over a display in the shop.

_____

_____

c) Elliott was watching the birds outside his window.

_____

_____

1 mark

20 Underline the **modal verbs** in the sentences below.

a) I cannot ride a bike.

b) You ought to visit your dentist regarding your cracked tooth.

c) May I speak with you?

d) I used to be able to do handstands.

e) I would have gone on the school trip, but I was unwell.

f) You don't have to do anything you don't want to.

1 mark

21 Fill in the gaps below, using the **past progressive** forms of the verbs in the boxes.

to revise

Whilst I _ _ _ _ _ _ _ _ _ for my upcoming musical assessment, my mum

to teach		to work

_ _ _ _ _ _ _ _ _ _ me a new piece to play on the piano. I _ _ _ _ _ _ _ _ _ _
really hard on it.

1 mark

22 Circle all the **determiners** in the sentence below.

*There were a few language errors in her writing, so I told her to
get a teacher to look over her work to get some feedback.*

1 mark

23 Which of the sentences below uses **dashes** in the correct manner? Tick **one**.

The girl was cute – beautiful, in fact I was envious –
of her looks.
☐

The girl was cute – beautiful, in fact – I was envious
of her looks.
☐

The girl was – cute – beautiful, in fact I was envious
of her looks.
☐

The girl – was cute beautiful, in fact – I was envious
of her looks.
☐

1 mark

24 Tick one box to show whether the sentence has been written in **past progressive** or **present progressive**.

SENTENCE	PAST PROGRESSIVE	PRESENT PROGRESSIVE
Rachel is continuously improving her hockey skills.		
Carl had been skateboarding with his friends after school.		
Ollie hopes to be an award-winning author.		
Teresa was sent out of the classroom for disrupting the class.		

1 mark

25 Draw a line to match each sentence with its correct **function**.

Check the travel updates before you set off on holiday

Are there any travel updates we should be aware of

I expect we will arrive in 2 hours if there are no delays

I can't wait for our holiday. It's going to be great

QUESTION

COMMAND

STATEMENT

EXCLAMATION

1 mark

26 Circle all of the **conjunctions** in the sentences below.

a) I love riding my bike and playing the piano.

b) You need to keep your coat on until we get indoors.

c) Do you want a tea or coffee, or perhaps a cold drink?

d) Although she was ill, she still sat her exam.

e) I had pizza for dinner, whereas my brother had lasagne.

f) Even though I was scared, I stayed there until the very end.

 27 Below is a list of homonyms. In the space provided, write down **two** different meanings of how that word can be used.

HOMONYM	MEANING 1	MEANING 2
Left		
Wave		
Watch		
Remote		

28 Five adjectives have been taken out of their place. Write the **adjectives** in the spaces below, in order for the passage to read correctly.

SERENE   BREATHTAKING   BEAUTIFUL   CALM   SPARKLY

The [ ] water was so peaceful. As the clear

water fell, the [ ] sounds added to the divine, soft illusion.

The water was [ ] and created a [ ]

reflection at the bottom of the cliffs. It was truly [ ].

[ ]

1 mark

29 Write the correct label in each box.

Verb (V)	Noun (N)	Connective (C)	Adjective (A)

[ ]   [ ]

The girl had an audition. She danced beautifully across the stage. However, she was unsuccessful.

[ ]   [ ]

[ ]

1 mark

30 Preston needs your help! He wants you to add a **prefix** to the following words, in order to change these words into their **antonyms**.

_ _ _ _ _ _ _ _ _ _ justice

_ _ _ _ _ _ _ _ _ _ polite

_ _ _ _ _ _ _ _ _ _ trust

_ _ _ _ _ _ _ _ _ _ behave

_ _ _ _ _ _ _ _ _ _ fortunate

_ _ _ _ _ _ _ _ _ _ regular

1 mark

31 Tick **one** of the boxes that means the **opposite** of:

Malicious

Intended harm.

Sympathetic.

Mischievous in motivation.

Enjoys embarrassing others.

1 mark

32 Tick the box to show whether the underlined word is a **coordinating conjunction** or a **subordinating conjunction.**

SENTENCE	COORDINATING CONJUNCTION	SUBORDINATING CONJUNCTION
When I go to the pub, I usually have burger _and_ chips.		
As long as it's not raining, we will go to the park.		
I am really looking forward to the summer _even though_ my friends are going away.		
I've never gone fishing, _nor_ do I ever plan to.		

1 mark

33 Circle whether you think the sentence is a **direct question** or **indirect question.**

a) Felicity asked me when I was next free

DIRECT / INDIRECT

b) Aren't you going to invite me in

DIRECT / INDIRECT

c) I wondered why you left without saying goodbye

DIRECT / INDIRECT

d) Will I get a raise

DIRECT / INDIRECT

e) He asked me which part of the lesson I didn't understand

DIRECT / INDIRECT

1 mark

34 Add **pairs of brackets** to the following sentences, in order to make them easier to read.

a) Jackie a shy, young girl loved spending time in her local library.

b) The two cats Molly and Pete were playing with a ball of string.

c) My sister who lives in New Zealand is coming to visit for 2 weeks.

d) The robber wanted to open the safe, but it was locked with a voice recognition code.

1 mark

 35 Underline the **subordinate clause** in the sentences below. The first one has been done for you.

Jamie loves watching football, especially when the team he supports is playing.

a) Even though he didn't have much time, Pete knew he could finish his work on time.

b) Mark and Jack finished their training, which was strenuous.

c) We made a decision, that for the weekend, my brother and I would visit our grandparents.

1 mark

36 Using the **conjunctions** listed below, match up the sentences on the left with the sentences on the right. <u>The first one has been done for you.</u>

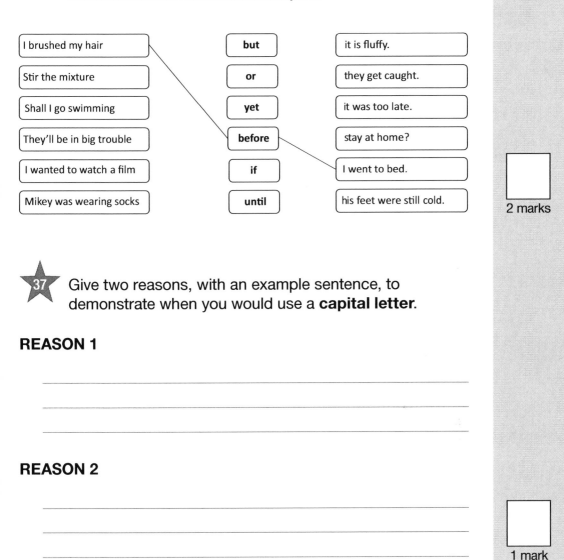

I brushed my hair		but		it is fluffy.
Stir the mixture		or		they get caught.
Shall I go swimming		yet		it was too late.
They'll be in big trouble		before		stay at home?
I wanted to watch a film		if		I went to bed.
Mikey was wearing socks		until		his feet were still cold.

2 marks

37 Give two reasons, with an example sentence, to demonstrate when you would use a **capital letter**.

REASON 1

_____

_____

_____

REASON 2

_____

_____

_____

1 mark

38 The following sentences need commas in order to make the sentences read coherently. Draw the **comma** in the correct place for each sentence. <u>More than one comma may be needed.</u>

a) Suddenly we heard a loud knock at the door.

b) Vinnie's mum had blown up blue green red and orange balloons.

c) Freddie a frightened young boy was scared to go to school.

d) "Listen up" shouted the teacher. She was getting very impatient with one student in particular.

 39 Tick the boxes which demonstrate the correct use of **apostrophes**.

Sammies' dog won an award for a dog talent contest. ☐

The children's clothes were wet from playing outside in the rain. ☐

It hasn't gone unnoticed. Savannah's work ethic is remarkable. ☐

The babie's push chair was too big to fit in the car. ☐

Its' been a long time since we last went to the cinema. ☐

The boys' locker rooms we're a mess. ☐

40 Circle the correct **verb** in order for the sentences to be written in **Standard English**.

I <u>never / didn't</u> break it.

I <u>did / done</u> it!

We <u>was / were</u> planning to go home the day after tomorrow.

I have <u>wrote / written</u> in my diary.

1 mark

 41 Add a **subordinate clause** to the following sentences.

The wind, _____, blew through the trees.

_____, the little boy started to cry.

The moon, _____, reflected in the ocean water.

The sun, _____, was beginning to fade.

1 mark

42 The word **'<u>she</u>'** is underlined. Explain why this word shouldn't be used in this sentence.

Maddie received her results and opened them with her mum.
<u>She</u> was over the moon.

_____

_____

_____

1 mark

43 Create a sentence using the word <u>cause</u> as a noun.

_____

_____

1 mark

Create a sentence using the word <u>cause</u> as a verb.

_____

_____

1 mark

 44 Underline the **noun phrase** in the sentence below.

The chewed-up dog bone was half buried in the mud.

1 mark

45 Underline the **adverbial phrase** in each of the below sentences.

1. No matter how difficult it is, I'm going to do my best.

2. In order to arrive on time, I have set my alarm.

3. Natalie will let us know as soon as they arrive.

4. Once a week, I attend ice skating lessons.

2 marks

46 Lalita needs your help. Match the words to their correct **antonym**.

WORD

FASCINATING

ABUNDANT

COMPASSION

CONFIDENTIAL

ANTONYM

ANIMOSITY

REVEALED

REPELLANT

SCARCE

1 mark

KEY STAGE 2
English

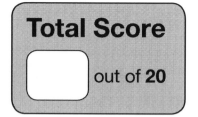

Total Score

out of **20**

SET A
Practice Paper 2
Grammar, Punctuation & Spelling

Spelling

15 minutes

First Name	
Middle Name/s	
Last Name	
School	
Date of Birth	*D D / M M / Y Y Y Y*

SPELLING

1. My best friend offered her _.

2. I was not _ of the circumstances.

3. I had to find some clothes that were _ _ _ _ _ _ _ _ _ _ _ _ _ _ _ _ _ _ _ for a wedding.

4. Our plans to go away for the weekend were not
    _.

5. I was asked to work on my _.

6. My father's _ was being a dentist.

7. There was not _ _ _ _ _ _ _ _ _ _ _ _ _ _ _ _ _ _ _ evidence to convict the suspect.

8. The _ _ _ _ _ _ _ _ _ _ _ _ _ _ _ _ _ _ boy was sent out of the classroom for bad behaviour.

9. It would be an _____ to meet the Queen.

10. The _____ of the perfume was flowery.

11. I was _____ for wearing trousers that were too big for me.

12. He was a _____, old man.

13. I was _____ for my handwriting.

14. My dad's _____ was stolen.

15. The young girl sounded _____.

16. It turned out to be a _____ trip.

17. My mum told me off for _____.

18. For my geography lesson, we looked at the _____.

19. I had to stand and _____ for a long time.

20. Two of the boys had to be _____ because they were fighting.

KEY STAGE 2
English

SET A
Practice Paper 3
Comprehension

Reading & Comprehension

1 hour

First Name	
Middle Name/s	
Last Name	
School	
Date of Birth	D D / M M / Y Y Y Y

VOLCANOES

CITY BY NIGHT

COUNTRYSIDE
BY DAY

PENGUINS

Read the text carefully and answer the following questions.

Volcanoes by How2Become.

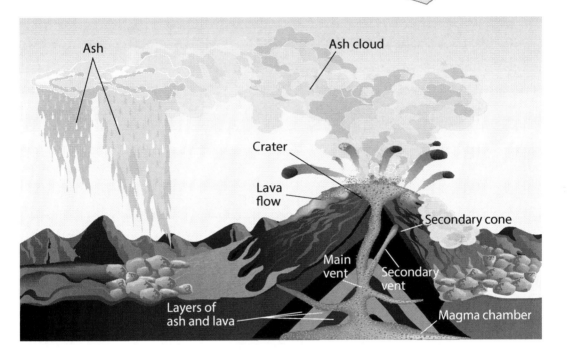

GLOSSARY

CRATER – indentation at the top of the volcano.

LAVA – a liquid rock that reaches Earth surface (flows outside the volcano).

MAGMA – a liquid, molten rock below Earth surface (inside the volcano).

MAGMA CHAMBER – large area underneath the Earth's surface, filled with magma.

VENT – opening in the top or side of volcano where lava erupts.

VOLCANIC ASH – tiny pieces of ash that are ejected into the air from a volcanic eruption.

WHAT IS A VOLCANO?

The origin of the word volcano comes from the word 'Vulcan' – a god of fire in Roman Mythology.

Most volcanoes are mountains and found in the Pacific Ocean. Magma and poisonous gases build up before exploding through the Earth's surface.

A volcano is a type of landform that opens downwards to a pool of molten rock (magma).

HOW ARE VOLCANOES FORMED?

The Earth has three layers – the crust (at the top), the mantle (the middle), and the core (the centre).

The formation of volcanoes is quite simple. When magma, from below the Earth's upper mantle, works its way to the surface, this creates an eruption.

DIFFERENT STAGES OF VOLCANOES

There are three main categories which define what kind of volcano it is – active, dormant and extinct.

An active volcano is a volcano that is or has erupted recently, and is likely to erupt again.

A dormant volcano is a volcano that has not erupted recently, but is likely to erupt.

An extinct volcano is a volcano that has not erupted and is not expected to erupt.

WHY DO VOLCANOES ERUPT?

Volcanoes erupt due to the friction between the plates of the Earth's crust. These 'tectonic plates' fit together like a jigsaw puzzle, and when these plates move, it causes the volcano to erupt.

Volcanoes are also suggested to trigger other natural disasters such as earthquakes, flooding, mud flows, rock falls and tsunamis.

EFFECTS OF VOLCANOES

Eruptions of volcanoes have long-lasting effects on both humans and the environment.

Some of the consequences following a volcano eruption include:

- Destroyed buildings;
- Destroyed habitats and landscapes;
- People becoming homeless;
- People being killed or seriously injured;
- Ash covering plants, making them inedible;
- Poisonous gases killing people and animals;
- Dark skies, strong winds and heavy rain may follow.

THE MAUNA LOA

The Mauna Loa (meaning Long Mountain) is the largest active shield volcano in the world. That means it's built almost entirely of fluid magma flows.

This volcano is one of five that forms the Island of Hawaii in the Pacific Ocean.

Having erupted over 33 times since 1843, the Mauna Loa is taller than Mount Everest if measured from its base below sea level to its summit.

Question 1

What is the difference between magma and lava?

_____

_____

_____

1 mark

Question 2

What are the three parts that make up the Earth's surface?

1. _____

2. _____

3. _____

1 mark

Question 3

Defeat our supervillain Blaze by matching the term with its definition. <u>The first one has been done for you.</u>

WORD

MANTLE

CRATER

VOLCANO

VULCAN

LAVA FLOW

DEFINITION

The circular indent around the vent, found at the top of the volcano.

'God of fire', meaning volcano.

Molten rock which streams down the outside of the volcano after an eruption.

The middle layer of the Earth.

A landform that opens downwards to a pool of molten rock.

2 marks

Question 4

The text uses a simile. What is the simile and explain how it ties in with the context of the passage.

_____

_____

_____

_____

_____

1 mark

Question 5

What type of literary text is this? Circle **one**.

INSTRUCTION EXPLANATION PERSUASION INFORMATIVE

Explain how you know this.

_____

_____

_____

1 mark

Question 6

For the following words, write the definition of each type of volcano.

ACTIVE

_____

_____

DORMANT

_____

_____

EXTINCT

_____

_____

1 mark

Question 7

Name **three** other natural disasters which could be triggered by a volcanic eruption.

1. _____

2. _____

3. _____

1 mark

Question 8

Explain the impact volcanic eruptions have on both humans and the environment. Use **examples** to support your answer.

_____

_____

_____

_____

_____

_____

_____

1 mark

Question 9

The writer lists the consequences of volcanic eruptions. How do you think the writer wants their readers to be feeling at this point?

_____

_____

_____

_____

1 mark

Question 10

Tick whether the statement is **true** or **false** based on the information provided in the text.

STATEMENT	TRUE	FALSE
The Mauna Loa means 'Long Mountain'.		
For a volcano to be dormant, it must have erupted recently.		
Most volcanoes are found in the Atlantic Ocean.		
The hot, liquid rock under the Earth's crust is called lava.		
Magma and poisonous gases build up before an eruption.		
Heavy rain and strong winds always occur after a volcanic eruption.		

2 marks

Question 11

The writer has provided a glossary. What is a glossary? Tick **one**.

A short introduction. ☐

A small dictionary. ☐

A short summary. ☐

A reference sheet. ☐

1 mark

Why do you think the writer has provided a glossary?

_____

_____

1 mark

Question 12

Complete the following sentences by selecting one of the words from the boxes below. <u>Each word can only be used once.</u>

MAGMA　　　**ASH**　　　**SUMMIT**

LAVA　　　**UPPER**　　　**CORE**

a) The crust is the _____ layer of Earth.

b) _____ is a liquid rock that flows out of the volcano.

c) The _____ is the highest point of a mountain.

d) The inner layer of Earth is called the _____.

e) _____ covers plants and makes them inedible.

f) Molten rock, also known as _____, can be found beneath the Earth's surface.

2 marks

Read the text carefully and answer the following questions.

Poems by How2Become.

COUNTRYSIDE BY DAY

Deep into the woods, where nothing is heard,
Except for the humming of an invisible bird.
Not a sound, nor whisper, nor spoken word.

An oak tree wrinkled for a 100 years,
The perfect post to shed your tears.
Supportive and strong - like it appears.

Next to the tree flowed a crystal clear stream,
A vision of beauty, a waking dream.
The yellow rays that beat and beamed.

Peaceful bliss, so solitude,
All my thoughts and ideas persued.
A place to think, a place to view.

These are the things the countryside bring,
Butterfly wings and birds that sing.
As precious as a royalty's ring.

High tree tops that offer protection,
A perfect time for self-reflection.
The sounds and wildlife is perfection.

A countryside by day.

CITY BY NIGHT

Walking along 1st avenue,
The sky above all dark and blue.
Hidden from the colourful lights,
Stars forbidden to shine so bright.

A city of people sleeping away,
Sleeping soundly, awaiting for day.
To me, though, the best part is the night,
Manhattan's magic comes into sight.

A city of life, and a city of beat,
The music that fills the lit-up street.
Never dull, never alone,
Never silent, never a drone.

A city of experience like I have never seen,
The energy, the vibes, the almighty gleam.
Everyone always moving fast-paced,
Yet they move with poise, they move with grace.

The city sounds heard after dark,
Buzzed through the empty, childless park.
Dreams, fantasies and hopes to achieve,
Makes me never want to leave.

A city by night.

Day & Night

Question 1

Describe the rhyme pattern of 'Countryside by Day'.

_____

_____

_____

1 mark

Question 2

Describe the rhyme pattern of 'City by Night'.

_____

_____

_____

1 mark

Question 3

Compare and contrast the sound imagery in both the 'Countryside by Day' and 'City by Night'. What do you think the poets are trying to convey?

_____

_____

_____

_____

_____

_____

_____

_____

_____

_____

2 marks

Question 4

What does the poet mean by "invisible bird"?

_____

_____

_____

1 mark

Question 5

Make up your own verse for 'Countryside by Day'. Remember to follow the same rhythmic structure as the poet.

Explain why you have chosen those words and how this ties in with the overall theme of the poem.

_____

_____

_____

_____

_____

_____

_____

2 marks

Question 6

Both poets use alliteration in their writing. Using **examples** from both poems, explain the impact this has on the reader.

_____

_____

_____

_____

_____

1 mark

49

Question 7

Anil needs your help. The poems use different literary techniques in their writing. Match the term up with the correct example. The examples will have been taken directly from the passages.

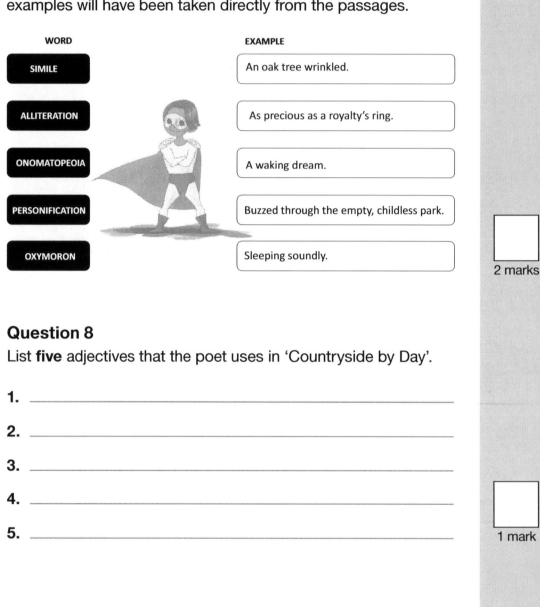

WORD

SIMILE

ALLITERATION

ONOMATOPEOIA

PERSONIFICATION

OXYMORON

EXAMPLE

An oak tree wrinkled.

As precious as a royalty's ring.

A waking dream.

Buzzed through the empty, childless park.

Sleeping soundly.

2 marks

Question 8

List **five** adjectives that the poet uses in 'Countryside by Day'.

1. _____

2. _____

3. _____

4. _____

5. _____

1 mark

Question 9

The poets compare night and day. They also compare city life to countryside life. Do you think you could use the rhythm and structure of these poems to write about something sad or upsetting? Circle **one**.

YES   **NO**

Explain your answer.

_____

_____

_____

_____

_____

1 mark

Question 10

Using the poem 'City by Night', offer a suggestion as to why you are unable to see the stars.

_____

_____

_____

_____

1 mark

Question 11

Explain how the poet of 'Countryside by Day' has given the tree human qualities. Use **examples** to support your answer.

_____

_____

_____

_____

_____

1 mark

Question 12

Describe the differences between the upbeat lifestyle in 'City by Night', with the calm, quiet lifestyle in 'Countryside by Day'.

How does the poet want you to feel? How do they convey this idea to their readers? Use examples from both poems to support your answer.

_____

_____

_____

_____

_____

_____

_____

_____

_____

_____

_____

2 marks

Read the text carefully and answer the following questions.

Penguins by How2Become.

ITEM 1

ADOPT A PENGUIN TODAY

HELP PENGUINS BY

- Reducing illegal fishing practices.
- Reducing greenhouse emissions.
- Raising awareness of climate change and penguin threats.
- Managing resources to safeguard their habitats.

READ ALL ABOUT PROTECTING **OUR** PENGUINS!

MEET SQUAWKS!

For just £3.00 a month, you can make the lives of Squawks and his friends so much better!

Your kind donations will go a long way to providing a safer, secure and happier life, which will help prolong the lives of penguin species.

Today, Adélie penguins face huge amounts of threats, many of which can be prevented, or managed in a more effective way. With threats on the increase, life as an Adélie penguin is proving difficult.

COMMON THREATS

Climate Change   Other penguins   Oil pollution

Overfishing   Snowy conditions

THE GENTOO

The Gentoo penguin is distributed mainly around the sub-Antarctic ocean, but also extends to places including the Antarctic Peninsula, Falklands, South Georgia, Macquarie Islands etc.

These penguins can be identified by their flamboyant red/orange beaks, peach-coloured feet, and white-feathered marking across the tops of their heads (the white stripe from one eye to the other). They are the third largest of penguins (after the King penguin and Emperor penguin), reaching a height of 30 inches.

They have adapted to very harsh living conditions. They use their wings to propel through the water reaching speeds of around 30mph. Krill, small crustaceans and larger organisms including squid, make up the Gentoo's diet.

A female Gentoo will generally breed once a year, laying two eggs, which are incubated by the faithful mother and father. Often, only one of the eggs hatch, and the penguin chick is fed and kept warm until they are around 3 months old.

This is a near-threatened animal. They are affected by the constant changes in water, temperature and pollution. In some areas, the Gentoo is also subject to human hunting.

THE EMPEROR

The Emperor penguin is the largest of all. These flightless animals live on Antarctic ice, where winds can plummet to temperatures of -60°C. Colonies huddle together to stay warm and protect themselves from these harsh weather conditions. The penguins will move to the interior of the huddle in order to get warm. Once they are toasty, they will move to the outer perimeter to allow their comrades the chance to get warm.

These penguins are the only bird to inhabit on open ice during the winter. During this time, the females will also breed. They will lay a single egg and then leave it behind to hunt for food. This can last up to two months, whereby they will have to walk in treacherous conditions. The male Emperor will keep the eggs warm, but they will not sit on them like other penguins. They will protect the eggs by standing their egg on their feet and covering it with their feathered-skin. The male penguin will not leave the egg's side until the female returns. During this time, the male penguin will not eat.

The female will return after her feast, and regurgitate her food to her baby chicks, whilst the male penguin can then be freed from babysitting to search for food himself.

To survive, these penguins are readily equipped: they have four layers of scale-like feathers, they can store large amounts of body fat, and their arteries and veins are close together to recycle their own body heat, which means blood is warmed up as it reaches the heart.

THE GALAPAGOS

The Galapagos penguin can be identified by their large bill and narrow white line around their face. They have a black head and a white border which runs from both sides of the face and meets at the base of their throat. Their belly is white with little black spots.

They are the northernmost of penguins and breed right on the equator. The name of this penguin derives from where they actually live. Colonies are found along the Galapagos Islands and the population of these type of penguins fluctuates a lot due to the 'El Niño' climate cycle. This cycle makes these penguins endangered. This climate cycle sees warm temperatures reaching the Equatorial Pacific.

They are a small penguin and are thought to be closely linked to the African penguin. The females breed once a year. She pairs off with someone and forms a bond for life. She will lay two eggs which are incubated, by both parents, for around 40 days. With only one egg usually hatching, the parents nurture and feed and keep the chick warm until it is around 1 years old.

The Galapagos penguin has adapted to their conditions in a number of ways. With their flippers extended when they stand, panting and seeking shade, these are just some of the ways they keep themselves cool.

There are less than 1,600 Galapagos penguin pairs left, and this is due to an upset in nature. El Niño, a lack of food, and a shortage of mating partners poses a threat to this species.

Question 1
What is the purpose of Item 1?

_____

_____

_____

1 mark

Question 2
Who do you think the text is aimed at?

_____

_____

_____

1 mark

Question 3
What was the name of the penguin that is introduced to us?

_____

1 mark

Question 4
In **Item 1**, why do you think the writer has used the word 'our' in the advertisement? What impact do you think this will have on the reader?

_____

_____

_____

_____

_____

1 mark

Question 5

Lalita needs your help! For the following statements, put a **tick** in the boxes to show whether the statement is **true** or **false**.

STATEMENT	TRUE	FALSE
The Galapagos penguin is the smallest of penguins.		
The Gentoo penguin is considered as highly endangered.		
The female Emperor penguin will leave her eggs to hunt for food.		
The Gentoo penguin can be identified by the black spots on their white bellies.		
The Emperor penguin is the only penguin to inhabit open ice during winters.		
El Niño is a climate cycle which brings in warm temperatures to the Equatorial Pacific.		

2 marks

Question 6

Other penguins are given as an example of threats to penguins. Explain why you think penguins can have a threat to the lives of other penguins.

_____

_____

_____

_____

_____

_____

2 marks

Question 7

In the passage about 'The Emperor', what does the term 'plummet' mean? Tick **one**.

A steep fall or drop.

A slow drop.

A steady increase.

A significant increase.

1 mark

Question 8

List 3 ways in which the Emperor penguin is equipped for the severe cold temperatures.

1. _____

2. _____

3. _____

1 mark

Question 9

How does the Emperor penguin stay warm?

_____

_____

_____

_____

_____

Question 10

By adopting a penguin, how will you be helping the penguins?

_____

_____

_____

_____

Question 11

The word 'fluctuate' means…

_____

_____

Question 12

How would you identify a Gentoo penguin?

_____

_____

_____

_____

Question 13

The word 'regurgitate' in regards to penguins means what?

_____

_____

1 mark

Question 14

What kind of text are the passages *'The Gentoo'*, *'The Emperor'* and *'The Galapagos'*? Circle **one**.

PERSUASIVE   INSTRUCTION   INFORMATIVE   DISCUSSION

Why do you think the writer has provided this information alongside the 'Adopt the penguin' advert?

_____

_____

_____

_____

_____

_____

2 marks

Question 15

Based on all of the information provided, do you think penguins are becoming extinct? Explain your answer using **examples** from the text.

_____

_____

_____

_____

_____

_____

1 mark

KEY STAGE 2
English

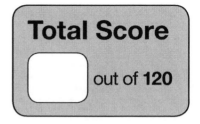

Total Score

out of **120**

SET A
Answer Booklet

Answers to Paper 1, Paper 2 and Paper 3

*Using the answers in this booklet, carefully add up the total marks for each paper. The total marks for each **SET** will be out of 120.*

You can use these marks to monitor your child's progression and work on their weaker areas.

	Paper 1 Mark out of 50	**Paper 2** Mark out of 20	**Paper 3** Mark out of 50	**TOTAL** Mark out of 120
SET A				

Paper 1

Q1. Disappear, Inactive, Commotion, Recite, Mislead — **1 mark**

Q2. *The words you should of circled are:* — **1 mark**
a) Quite
b) Loose
c) Our
d) Weak
e) Ewe

Q3. I think **I've** forgot where our car is parked. I **can't** see it. — **1 mark**

We **aren't** allowed to go beyond this point. **We'll** be in really big trouble.

Q4. *Your answer should look like this:* — **2 marks**

(2 marks for all correct answers. Award 1 mark for one or more answers incorrect).

SENTENCE	VERB	ADVERB	ADJECTIVE
The **hairy** man who sat in the corner.			✔
I **accepted** the consequences.	✔		
I had to **identify** an unusual insect.	✔		
The duck **gracefully** swum across the pond.		✔	
I **always** check over my homework.		✔	
My friend was **questioned** by the police.	✔		

Q5. — **1 mark**

1. Andy was a <u>spontaneous</u> man. He was <u>confident</u> and <u>enthusiastic</u> and liked to seek adventures.
2. The <u>courageous</u> 90 year old woman was praised for her bravery.

3. The thunder storm sounded <u>angry</u> and <u>violent</u>.
4. It was a <u>cunning</u> plan, and no one would be any the wiser.

Q6. Build

Q7. "Is it dinner time yet?" shouted Elizabeth, who was eager to eat.

The jury finally reached a verdict – not guilty.

1 mark

Q8. Harrison Blake (Chairman of the Football Committee) has decided to resign after 6 years.

1 mark

Q9. This necklace is **mine**.

1 mark

Q10.
a) The cat's tail.
b) Ryan's shoes are old and dirty.
c) The women's prams.

1 mark

Q11. Come back at the end of the day; I will have made a decision.

1 mark

Q12.
1. Can **you** all listen to the following instructions?
2. It wasn't **theirs** to give away.
3. It was **his** decision.
4. The car was at the garage because **it** needed fixing.

1 mark

Q13. Your answer should look like this:

ADJECTIVE	COMPARATIVE	SUPERLATIVE
Bright	Brighter	Brightest
Fine	Finer	Finest
Funny	Funnier	Funniest
Brave	Braver	Bravest
Friendly	Friendlier	Friendliest
Beautiful	More beautiful	Most beautiful

1 mark

Q14. The first sentence uses the commas to separate the 'which live in Africa'. This sentence is implying that all mountain gorillas live in Africa. The second sentence implies that only the mountain gorillas in Africa are endangered.

1 mark

Q15.

a) Cosy
   Snug
b) Clear
   Evident
c) Strange
   Unusual

1 mark

Q16.

a) Unlikely
   Uncertain
b) Melancholy
   Sad
c) Lie
   Fabrication

1 mark

Q17. Your answer should look like this:

Sentence	Main Clause	Subordinate Clause
Polly, **a year younger than me**, had to stay at home.		✔
Mr Smith, **who was Head of PE**, is leaving.		✔
After she picks me up, **my sister it taking me to get some ice cream**.	✔	
Although I was scared, **I walked into the room**.	✔	

1 mark

Q18.

a) Daniel knocked over the cereal box.

b) Sam kicked the ball over the fence.

c) The boy washed the windows.

1 mark

Q19.

a) Ella was told a secret by Gina.

b) The display in the shop was pushed over by the child.

c) Outside the window, the birds were being watched by Elliott.

1 mark

Q20.

a) I <u>cannot</u> ride a bike.

b) You <u>ought</u> to visit your dentist regarding your cracked tooth.

c) <u>May</u> I speak with you?

d) I <u>used</u> to be able to do handstands.

e) I <u>would have</u> gone on the trip, but I was unwell.

f) You <u>don't have</u> to do anything you don't want to.

1 mark

Q21. Whilst I **revised** for my upcoming musical assessment, my mum **taught** me a new piece to play on the piano. I **worked** really hard on it.

1 mark

Q22. The following words would need to be circled/highlighted:

There were a <u>few</u> language errors in <u>her</u> writing, so <u>I</u> told <u>her</u> to get a teacher to look over <u>her</u> work to get <u>some</u> feedback.

1 mark

Q23. The girl was cute – beautiful, in fact – I was envious of her looks.

1 mark

Q24. Your answer should look like this:

1 mark

SENTENCE	PAST PROGRESSIVE	PRESENT PROGRESSIVE
Rachel is continuously improving her hockey skills.		✔
Carl had been skateboarding with his friends after school.	✔	
Ollie hopes to be an award-winning author.		✔
Teresa was sent out of the classroom for disrupting the class.	✔	

Q25.

Check the travel updates before you set off on holiday **COMMAND**

Are there any travel updates we should be aware of? **QUESTION**

I expect we will arrive in 2 hours if there are no delays **STATEMENT**

I can't wait for our holiday. It's going to be great **EXCLAMATION**

1 mark

Q26.

a) I love riding my bike **and** playing the piano.

b) You need to keep your coat on **until** we get indoors.

c) Do you want a tea **or** coffee, **or perhaps** a cold drink?

d) **Although** she was ill, she still sat her exam.

1 mark

e) I had pizza for dinner, **whereas** my brother had lasagne.

f) **Even though** I was scared, I stayed there **until** the very end.

Q27. Left = as in the direction (turning left) OR being left behind.	**1 mark**

Wave = the waves of the ocean OR waving with your hand.

Watch = to watch something OR an item that tells you the time.

Remote = a control used to change channels OR a word to describe somewhere that is isolated.

Q28. The words should be written in the spaces, in this order:	**1 mark**

Calm   serene   beautiful   sparkly   breathtaking

Q29. Girl = noun (N)	**1 mark**

Danced = verb (V)

However = connective (C)

Unsuccessful = adjective (A)

Q30.	**1 mark**

Injustice

Impolite

Distrust

Misbehave

Unfortunate

Irregular

Q31. Sympathetic	**1 mark**

Q32. Your answer should look like this:

SENTENCE	COORDINATING CONJUNCTION	SUBORDINATING CONJUNCTION
When I go to the pub, I usually have burger and chips.	✔	
As long as it's not raining, we will go to the park.		✔
I am really looking forward to the summer even though my friends are going away.		✔
I've never gone fishing, nor do I ever plan to.	✔	

1 mark

Q33.

a) Indirect

b) Direct

c) Indirect

d) Direct

e) Indirect

1 mark

Q34.

a) Jackie (a shy, young girl) loved spending time in her local library.

b) The two cats (Molly and Pete) were playing with a ball of string.

c) My sister (who lives in New Zealand) is coming to visit for 2 weeks.

d) The robber wanted to open the safe, but it was locked (with a voice recognition code).

1 mark

Q35.

a) Even though he didn't have much time, Pete knew he could finish his work on time.

b) Mark and Jack finished their training, which was strenuous.

c) We made a decision, that for the weekend, my brother and I would visit our grandparents.

1 mark

Q36. Stir the mixture **until** it is fluffy. Shall I go swimming **or** stay at home? They'll be in big trouble **if** they get caught. I wanted to watch a film **but** it was too late. Mikey was wearing socks **yet** his feet were still cold.	**2 marks** (2 marks for all correct answers. Award 1 mark for one or more errors).
Q37. **Reason 1** = you would use a capital letter to begin new sentences. *(You need to write any sentence and begin it with a capital letter).* **Reason 2** = proper nouns begin with a capital letter. *(You need to write any sentence and use a proper noun (a name or place name) in your example).*	**1 mark**
Q38. a) Suddenly, we heard a loud knock at the door. b) Vinnie's mum had blown up blue, green, red and orange balloons. c) Freddie, a frightened, young boy was scared to go to school. d) "Listen up," shouted the teacher. She was getting very impatient, with one student in particular.	**1 mark**
Q39. The boxes you should have ticked should correspond with the following sentences: *The children's clothes were wet from playing outside in the rain.* *It hasn't gone unnoticed. Savannah's work ethic is remarkable.*	**1 mark**

Q40. Didn't Did Were Written	**1 mark**
Q41. You could have added any sentence to these, so long as it provides extra information. For example: • *The wind, strong and cold, blew through the trees.* • *Sat in the corner, the little boy started to cry.* • *The moon, which shone brightly, reflected in the ocean water.* • *The sun, peering over the hilltops, was beginning to fade.*	**1 mark**
Q42. The word 'she' is underlined because it is not clear who it is talking about. Is it talking about Maddie or her mum?	**1 mark**
Q43. You could have come up with any sentence, so long as you used the word 'cause' in the correct way. <u>For example:</u> They were trying to work out the **cause** of the explosion. = NOUN The icy roads could **cause** huge traffic delays. = VERB	**2 marks** (1 mark for each correct sentence.)
Q44. <u>The chewed-up dog bone</u> was half buried in the mud.	**1 mark**

Q45.	**2 marks**
1. <u>No matter</u> how difficult it is, I'm going to do my best.	(2 marks for all correct answers. Award 1 mark for no more than two errors).
2. <u>In order to</u> arrive on time, I have set my alarm.	
3. Natalie will let us know <u>as soon as</u> they arrive.	
4. <u>Once a week</u>, I attend ice skating lessons.	
Q46. Fascinating = repellent	**1 mark**
Abundant = scarce	
Compassion = animosity	
Confidential = revealed	

Paper 2

Spelling 1 = advice

Spelling 2 = aware

Spelling 3 = suitable

Spelling 4 = definite

Spelling 5 = pronunciation

Spelling 6 = profession

Spelling 7 = sufficient

Spelling 8 = mischievous

Spelling 9 = honour

Spelling 10 = scent

Spelling 11 = ridiculed

Spelling 12 = pretentious

Spelling 13 = criticised

Spelling 14 = vehicle

Spelling 15 = sincere

Spelling 16 = disastrous

Spelling 17 = exaggerating

Spelling 18 = environment

Spelling 19 = queue

Spelling 20 = separated

Paper 3

[Volcanoes]

Q1. Magma is the liquid of molten rock that can be found inside the volcano, whereas lava is the liquid that flows outside of the volcano.

1 mark

Q2. The crust, the mantle and the core

1 mark

Q3. Your answer should look like this:

2 marks

(2 marks for all correct answers. Award 1 mark for no more than two errors).

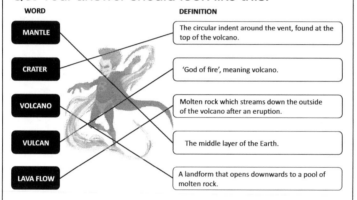

WORD	DEFINITION
MANTLE	The circular indent around the vent, found at the top of the volcano.
CRATER	'God of fire', meaning volcano.
VOLCANO	Molten rock which streams down the outside of the volcano after an eruption.
VULCAN	The middle layer of the Earth.
LAVA FLOW	A landform that opens downwards to a pool of molten rock.

Q4. "These 'tectonic plates' fit together like a jigsaw puzzle". This demonstrates the function of the tectonic plates and how they work together in order to create an overall impact.

1 mark

Q5. Informative

The text is informative as it is teaching you facts about volcanoes – it is documenting information about a particular subject. It uses technical language, facts and diagrams to inform its reader about the topic.

1 mark

Q6. Active = a volcano that is or has erupted recently, and is likely to erupt again.

Dormant = a volcano that has not erupted recently, but is likely to erupt.

Extinct = a volcano that has not erupted and is not expected to erupt.

1 mark

Q7. Earthquakes, flooding, tsunami

1 mark

Q8. Volcanic eruptions have a huge impact on both humans and the environment. Not only are people injured or killed during volcanic eruptions, but homes are lost and habitats are destroyed. Animals and plants have to re-adapt to deal with the ash and damaged grounds, which the majority are unable to cope with.

1 mark

Q9. The writer lists the consequences of volcanic eruptions in order to make the reader think about the impact eruptions have on humans and the environment. It makes the readers sympathise with the victims and understand the damage caused by natural disasters.

1 mark

Q10. Your answer should look like this:

STATEMENT	TRUE	FALSE
The Mauna Loa means 'Long Mountain'.	✔	
For a volcano to be dormant, it must have erupted recently.		✔
Most volcanoes are found in the Atlantic Ocean.		✔
The hot, liquid rock under the Earth's crust is called lava.		✔
Magma and poisonous gases build up before an eruption.	✔	
Heavy rain and strong winds always occur after a volcanic eruption.		✔

2 marks

(2 marks for all correct answers. Award 1 mark for no more than two errors).

Q11. A small dictionary

The writer has provided a glossary in order to provide the key terms and definitions about volcanoes and eruptions. This allows the reader to understand the important facts that they need to learn.

2 marks

(1 marks for correct reason an. 1 mark for explaining why it's used).

Q12.

a) The crust is the **upper** layer of Earth.

b) **Lava** is a liquid rock that flows out of the volcano.

c) The **summit** is the highest point of a mountain.

d) The inner layer of Earth is called the **core**.

e) **Ash** covers plants and makes them inedible.

f) Molten rock, also known as **magma**, can be found beneath the Earth's surface.

2 marks

(2 marks for all correct answers. Award 1 mark for no more than two errors).

Q1. The rhyme pattern of 'Countryside by Day' uses stanzas of three lines, and each stanza rhymes. For example, in the first stanza, the lines end with the words 'heard', 'bird' and 'word'. This creates a rhythmic flow.	**1 mark**
Q2. The rhyme pattern of 'City by Night' uses stanzas of four lines, of which the 1st and 2nd line rhyme, and the 3rd and 4th line rhyme. For example, in the first stanza, the 1st and 2nd lines rhyme with 'avenue' and 'blue'. The 3rd and 4th lines rhyme with 'lights' and 'bright'.	**1 mark**
Q3. The sound imagery conveyed in the poems are very different to one another. In the 'City by Night' it explores 'music' and 'beat' which creates an upbeat image. Whereas in the 'Countryside of Day', the sound imagery is conveyed as being 'peaceful bliss' and where 'nothing is heard'. The poets are trying to contrast day with night, by comparing a world of solitude and peace with an upbeat life.	**2 marks** (2 marks to be awarded for comparison and using examples. Award 1 mark for an attempt to compare with no reference or examples from the poems).
Q4. The poet uses the term "invisible bird" to suggest that the person is unable to see the bird, but is able to hear it. The term is not used to suggest the bird as literally being invisible, it is just a way of saying that it cannot be seen.	**1 mark**
Q5. *You could have made up any verse for the poem, as long as it fits in with the narrative and rhythmic structure. You would need to explain why you have carefully chosen those words and how it links in with the rest of the poem.	**2 marks** (2 marks for a solid attempt at a verse, using the same rhythmic structure and narrative).

For example:

Beyond the trees stood a wild deer,
Without a care, without a fear.
Pranced off so fast in upper gear.

You could say that you chose the word deer because it ties in with the nature and setting of the poem. You followed the rhythmic structure of the poem, creating an image of nature, idealism and tranquillity.

Q6. Alliteration is a powerful literary tool which not only creates rhythm, but also makes it more memorable. For example, in 'City by Night', the poet uses alliterated phrases of 'sleeping soundly' and 'Manhattan's magic'. The poem 'Countryside by Day' uses the alliterations of 'royalty's ring' and 'crystal clear' to make the poems more descriptive and rhythmic.

1 mark

Q7. Your answer should look like this:

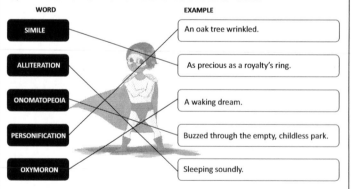

WORD | EXAMPLE

SIMILE

ALLITERATION

ONOMATOPEOIA

PERSONIFICATION

OXYMORON

An oak tree wrinkled.

As precious as a royalty's ring.

A waking dream.

Buzzed through the empty, childless park.

Sleeping soundly.

2 marks

(2 marks awarded for all correct answers. Award 1 mark for no more than two errors).

Q8. Perfect, supportive, strong, precious, peaceful.

1 mark

Q9. *Your answer could be anything, so long as you back your answer with justified reasons. For example: *You could have circled no. You could justify your response by saying how the rhythmic pattern of these poems is upbeat and positive, and this would not work for a narrative that is on something sad or upsetting.*	**1 mark**
Q10. You are unable to see the stars because of all of the lights that appear in the city. These bright 'colourful' lights ignite the sky and therefore make it hard to see the stars.	**1 mark**
Q11. The poem 'Countryside by Day' has given the tree human qualities, by referring to it as if it was an old person. For example, the tree is described as having 'wrinkled for a 100 years', which implies its age. It is also described as being 'supportive' which is also a human characteristic.	**1 mark**
Q12. The poem 'City by Night' is described in a positive and upbeat way. The poet describes the city as a 'city of life, and a city of beat' which emphasises how the city never sleeps. The poet focuses on visuals of people moving fast-paced and energy and vibes, and the sounds of music and beat demonstrates the city as 'never silent, never a drone'. The poem 'Countryside by Day' uses a lot of visuals to describe the nature of the woods as peaceful. The calming effects of the water, the quietness and beauty of the wildlife all add to the calming image.	**2 marks** (2 marks awarded for using examples and describing the differences between the poems. Award 1 mark with a poor attempt at describing the poems, with little or no support from the text).

[Penguins]

Q1. The purpose of Item 1 is to persuade people to adopt a penguin. It is a persuasive text which is encouraging the reader to do something active by supporting the penguins.

1 mark

Q2. The text is aimed at people who love wildlife and want to help. Because it is asking for money, this text is aimed at people who are able to help. It is aimed at people who like penguins and conservation.

1 mark

Q3. Squawks

1 mark

Q4. The writer uses the word 'our' in order to draw the reader in. Appealing directly to the reader makes them think that they have an active part in this. It allows the reader to think about the message being portrayed and engages them instantly with the topic being discussed.

1 mark

Q5. Your answer should look like this:

2 marks

(2 marks for all correct answers. Award 1 mark for no more than two errors).

STATEMENT	TRUE	FALSE
The Galapagos penguin is the smallest of penguins.		✔
The Gentoo penguin is considered as highly endangered.		✔
The female Emperor penguin will leave her eggs to hunt for food.	✔	
The Gentoo penguin can be identified by the black spots on their white bellies.		✔
The Emperor penguin is the only penguin to inhabit open ice during winters.	✔	
El Niño is a climate cycle which brings in warm temperatures to the Equatorial Pacific.	✔	

Q6. Other penguins could pose a threat to penguins. If some penguins adapt to climate change, but others don't, then the latter penguins could lose their territory, food and shelter to the former.	**2 marks** (2 marks for a strong attempt to justify a reasons. Award 1 mark for poor reasoning).
Q7. A steep fall or drop	**1 mark**
Q8. Four layers of scale-like feathers, they can store large amounts of body fat, and their arteries and veins are close together in order to recycle their own body heat.	**1 mark**
Q9. The Emperor penguin stays warm via the body heat of other penguins. They huddle together in their colonies. Once they are warm, they will move to the outer perimeter of the huddle to allow other penguins to get warm.	**1 mark**
Q10. Reduce illegal fishing practices, reduce greenhouse emissions, raising awareness of climate change and penguin threats, improve and manage resources to safeguard their habitats.	**1 mark**
Q11. The word 'fluctuate' means to change continuously. The Galapagos penguin population fluctuates (goes up and down) a lot due to El Niño.	**1 mark**
Q12. You can identify a Gentoo penguin by their red/orange beaks, peach-coloured feet and white-feathered marking across the top of their heads.	**1 mark**
Q13. The word 'regurgitate' means bringing swallowed food back up again in order to feed their chicks.	**1 mark**

Q14. Informative	**2 marks**
The writer has provided informative text alongside their persuasive text in order to make their appeal more convincing. The persuasive text engages the reader emotionally in the penguins' struggle, while the informative text gives the reader specific and factual reasons for why they should adopt and help protect them.	(1 mark for circling the correct text, and 1 mark for providing reasons as to why the writer has used both type of texts).
Q15. *This is based on personal opinion. Your answer can be anything so long as you support your reasoning with examples from the text.	**1 mark**

Q15. *This is based on personal opinion. Your answer can be anything so long as you support your reasoning with examples from the text.

For example:

You could say that you believe penguins are becoming extinct. The dramatic climate changes are having a huge effect on their icy environments. The fact that their food source is being taken by humans, means this is impacting on the food chain, suggesting that if this continues, the penguins will run out of food supply.

[END OF SET A]

KEY STAGE 2 English

Total Score

out of **50**

SET B Practice Paper 1

Grammar, Punctuation & Spelling

Questions

45 minutes

First Name	
Middle Name/s	
Last Name	
School	
Date of Birth	*D D / M M / Y Y Y Y*

1 Underline the correct **homophones** for the following sentences.

a) Julie asked for a (peace, piece) of cake.

b) My mum went to the bank and had to (cue, queue) for an hour.

c) (Their, There, They're) going to need a bigger boat.

1 mark

 2 Which of the following sentences has a **mistake** in its punctuation?

A – Everyone came to my party – except Jason.

B – What is the capital city of Italy?

C – If I could be any animal, I would be an eagle.

D – "Stop it?" shouted the teacher.

E – I drank a lot of fizzy drink at the party; it made me feel sick.

Answer ⬚

1 mark

3 Complete these words by adding the prefixes **mis** or **dis**.

------connect ------lead ------treat ------understood

------honest ------ability ------loyal ------print

1 mark

4 Defeat the enemy! Blaze has written these sentences to try and catch you out! The underlined words in the sentences below are incorrect. Change them to a correct verb.

Read the sentences and write them out in Standard English.

a) My teacher <u>give</u> me detention.

_____

b) Lilly <u>were</u> going to Italy during the summer holidays.

_____

c) My dad <u>teached</u> me how to swim.

_____

d) Blaze, <u>whose</u> an evil villain, is planning revenge.

_____

1 mark

5 Tick the box to show whether the highlighted word is a **verb**, **adverb** or **adjective**.

SENTENCE	VERB	ADVERB	ADJECTIVE
Henry **declared** his love of football.			
Jordan **scoffed** down his gummy bears.			
Joshua came to work every morning **determined** to succeed.			
Richard **sang** really loudly.			
Gemma walked around the room **graciously**.			
Katie **always** got to work early.			

1 mark

6 Write the **past** tense of the following words.

buy	shake	think	lay	leave	find

1 mark

7 For the following words, write down an **alternative** word that **sounds** the same but has a different meaning.

Son _____   Flour _____

Meet _____   Whose _____

None _____   Chews _____

Red _____   So _____

For _____   Blue _____

1 mark

8 For the following questions, you need to work out the **correct spelling** of the word. Please circle your chosen answer.

a) It is _ _ _ _ _ _ _ _ _ _ _ _ _ _ _ the coldest day of the year.

DEFIANTLY   DEFINATELY   DEFINITELY   DEFENATLY

b) The _ _ _ _ _ _ _ _ _ _ _ _ _ _ wanted to talk to the whole school.

PRINCEAPLE   PRINCIPLE   PRINCAPLE   PRINCIPAL

c) The argument played on Millie's _ _ _ _ _ _ _ _ _ _ _ _ _ _ _ _ _ _.

CONSCIENCE   CONSHANCE   CONSCEINCE   CONSCIOUS

1 mark

9 Rewrite the sentences adding/deleting **apostrophes** where appropriate.

a) The cats bed was full of cat hair.

_____

b) The babys nappy needed to be changed.

_____

c) This wasnt the best idea. My mums car was wrecked.

_____

d) The horses that belonged to the jockey's.

_____

e) The childrens toys, that were at my Aunties house, were all over her floor.

_____

2 marks

88

10 The power of clauses! Blaze needs your help! Rewrite the sentences below adding a **relative clause**. Remember to punctuate the sentence so that it reads correctly.

a) My father went fishing.

_____

_____

b) Rachel was late home from school.

_____

_____

c) Leah went to the school disco.

_____

_____

d) Charlie and Megan played on the swings.

_____

_____

1 mark

11 Tick the box to say whether the bold statement is a **main clause** or **subordinate clause**.

Sentence	Main Clause	Subordinate Clause
Although I was scared of the water, I jumped in the pool.		
My best friend is expecting a baby; I'm happy for her.		
Blaze shoots fire from his hands – **an impressive superpower!**		
When the teacher turned her back, **the students would throw paper around.**		

1 mark

12 Create 3 sentences using **hyphens**.

1) ....

2) ....

3) ....

1 mark

Create 3 sentences using **dashes**.

1) ....

2) ....

3) ....

1 mark

Explain the difference between **hyphens** and **dashes** and discuss when you would use each one.

....

....

....

....

....

1 mark

13 Scarlett needs your help! Fill in the gaps with either
practice/practise or **advice/advise**.

a) The school choir had _ _ _ _ _ _ _ _ _ _ _ _ _ _ _ _ _ _ _
three times a week.

b) I need some _ _ _ _ _ _ _ _ _ _ _ _ _ _ _ _ _ _
about what to do.

c) I need to _ _ _ _ _ _ _ _ _ _ _ _ _ _ _ _ _ _
my dance moves.

d) I _ _ _ _ _ _ _ _ _ _ _ _ _ _ _ _ you to take your
time and think about it very carefully.

e) My brother tries to _
his football every day, but sometimes is late
to his football _.

1 mark

14 Identify which suffixes can be used with the words below.
Tick the boxes where the suffix can be joined to the word.

The first one has been done for you: as you can see,
some can take more than one!

	- Ist	- Ism	- Ery
Art	✔		✔
Tour			
Cook			
Real			
Station			

1 mark

15 Tick **two** sentences where the **subject** and the **verb** agree correctly.

The man cycle to work every day. ☐

Everyone I know are going to the party. ☐

Matt and James like playing hockey. ☐

Rachel and Susie was not being nice. ☐

It was time that I went to bed. ☐

☐ 2 marks

16 Complete the words by adding **–cial** or **–tial.**

For each word, work out how many **syllables** there are. <u>The first one has been done for you.</u>

	ADD –CIAL OR –TIAL	SYLLABLES	NUMBER OF SYLLABLES
Confiden_____	Confidential	Con-fi-den-tial	4
Essen_____			
Cru_____			
Finan_____			
Ini_____			
Par_____			

☐ 2 marks

17 Lalita is learning all about silent letters. Using the words in the box provided, **underline** the silent letter.

Subtle	Scissors	Guide
Castle	Christmas	Biscuit
Isle	Hour	When
Lamb	Rhino	White
Wrap	Hedge	Gnome

2 marks

 18 For the following sentences, rewrite the sentence correcting any punctuation or spelling errors. Look out for capital letters, punctuation marks and grammatical errors.

1. only 30 centimetres in height, meerkats depend on group coperation to survive in the kalahari desert. One meerkat will stand up on its hind legs (propped up by it's tail) and act as a lookout while the others look for food

_____

_____

_____

2. areas of outstanding natural beauty (AONB) are landscapes that offer beauty and nature and need safeguarding. These AONBs inclue rocky shores sand dunes saltmarshes sanday beaches cliffs and many more

_____

_____

_____

3. during world war II children were evactuated to protect them from air raids children were mainly sent to the countryside where their were less risks of air raids these children were taken in by familys across the country

_____

_____

_____

3 marks

19 For the following sentences, rewrite the sentences to change the **active voices** into **passive voice**.

ACTIVE VOICE	PASSIVE VOICE
I made a paper aeroplane.	
Elaine cut the grass.	
The cat scratched the girl.	
I have finished my homework.	

1 mark

20 For the following sentences, rewrite the sentences to change the **passive voices** into **active voices**

PASSIVE VOICE	ACTIVE VOICE
The kitchen is cleaned by Martin.	
The customer was being helped by the sales assistant.	
The car was stolen by Jim.	
The bike was repaired by Damien.	

1 mark

21 Add **alliterative adjectives** in the spaces provided.

a) The _ _ _ _ _ _ _ _ _ _ _ _ _ _ _ _ bees were hovering around the park.

b) The _ _ _ _ _ _ _ _ _ _ _ _ _ _ _ elves were dressed in

_ _ _ _ _ _ _ _ _ _ _ _ _ _ _ clothes.

c) We watched the _ _ _ _ _ _ _ _ _ _ _ _ _ _ stars using a

_ _ _ _ _ _ _ _ _ _ _ _ _ _ telescope.

d) We got to touch the _ _ _ _ _ _ _ _ _ _ _ _ _ _ elephant. It was

_ _ _ _ _ _ _ _ _ _ _ _ _ _ amazing.

1 mark

22 Insert the **modal verbs** in order for the sentences to
make sense. For each sentence, circle whether the modal
verb indicates **possibility** or **certainty.**

Will be	Should	Can	Might

1. It _ _ _ _ _ _ _ _ _ _ _ _ _ _ be possible.

POSSIBILITY / CERTAINTY

2. _ _ _ _ _ _ _ _ _ _ _ _ _ _ I do my homework?

POSSIBILITY / CERTAINTY

3. It _ _ _ _ _ _ _ _ _ _ _ _ _ _ be cold tomorrow.

POSSIBILITY / CERTAINTY

4. Yasmin _ _ _ _ _ _ _ _ _ _ _ _ _ _ play the piano.

POSSIBILITY / CERTAINTY

1 mark

95

23 Blaze has given you a conquest! Underline ALL of the **verbs** in the sentences below.

1. The birds flew gracefully in the sky.

2. The glass table, which was made by Sam's neighbour, was smashed to pieces.

3. Blaze jumped from rooftop to rooftop. He searched for the superheroes, who he was trying to defeat.

4. I laughed and smiled a lot. My best friend makes me feel incredibly happy.

1 mark

 24 Create your own sentences, using the following **conjunctions**.

Nor

_____

_____

Except

_____

_____

But

_____

_____

Despite

_____

_____

1 mark

25 Below are three statements about using apostrophes. Circle whether the statement is **true** or **false**.

a) If you use the word **ITS**, you are showing that something belongs to someone or something.

TRUE / FALSE

b) Names ending in 'S' will only need an apostrophe when demonstrating possession.

TRUE / FALSE

c) The following sentence uses the apostrophe correctly: "My neighbours' cars are always parked outside my house."

TRUE / FALSE

1 mark

 26 Rewrite the following sentences adding in all **missing punctuation**.

a) We need to get a move on said Harry

b) Rob asked can I stay outside and play for 10 more minutes

c) The report said the school encouraged childrens learning in a fun and unique way

d) I was terrified I didnt know what to do said a young frightened boy

2 marks

27 Explain the difference between **informal** and **formal** writing. Give an example of when you would use each.

_____

_____

_____

EXAMPLE 1

_____

EXAMPLE 2

_____

3 marks

28 The sentence below contains **nouns** and **adjectives**. Write two of each in the spaces provided.

Vincent rehearsed an energetic Salsa dance. He had to wear a sequinned shirt.

ADJECTIVE 1	ADJECTIVE 2	NOUN 1	NOUN 2

1 mark

29 Write **two examples** of a command and **two examples** of an exclamation.

COMMAND 1

_____

COMMAND 2

_____

EXCLAMATION 1

_____

EXCLAMATION 2

_____

2 marks

30 Freddie needs your help! Write the word **phrase** or **clause** to demonstrate whether the highlighted words are a phrase or a clause.

WORD   CLAUSE OR PHRASE?

Everyone clapped after the performance.

We all stood, **with a sigh of relief,** when we got the news.

I am studying Medicine at university; I want to help people.

Even though it was cold, **we went to the beach.**

2 marks

31 Tick **two** boxes that shows the sentence using the correct **plural**.

When the moon came out, the wolfs were roaming around the woods.

The baby was crying because she had two teeth coming through.

The childs were playing quietly together.

This country was known for having many volcanoes.

The gooses were very protective of their offspring.

2 marks

99

32 In the sentence below, **circle** the fronted adverbial. **Underline** all other adverbs.

As quick as a flash, the cheetah ran through the wild. He sprinted elegantly, powerfully, and with determination.

1 mark

 33 Insert a **pair of commas** to show parenthesis.

My friends from school all of whom I am still in contact with have arranged a party before everyone leaves for university.

1 mark

 34 Using the letters in each box, write them in the correct box to indicate what type of word each one is.

NOUN (N)	ADJECTIVE (A)	VERB (V)	ADVERB (AV)	PROPER NOUN (PN)

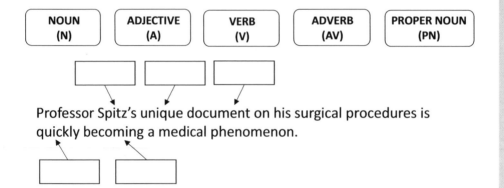

Professor Spitz's unique document on his surgical procedures is quickly becoming a medical phenomenon.

2 marks

 35 Replace the underlined word with a **synonym**.

After 90 minutes, the football players were <u>tired</u>.

1 mark

KEY STAGE 2 English

SET B
Practice Paper 2
Grammar, Punctuation & Spelling

Spelling

15 minutes

First Name	
Middle Name/s	
Last Name	
School	
Date of Birth	D D / M M / Y Y Y Y

SPELLING

1. My mum and dad were having an _____.

2. My best friend's birthday is in _____.

3. I _____ that everything happens for a reason.

4. It was a _____ Monday morning.

5. I got into trouble _____ I was not listening.

6. My History lessons were the most _____.

7. It was _____ responsibility.

8. The room in _____ house was big and empty.

9. The _____ of going to school was unbearable.

10. My brother and I are extremely _.

11. We planned a _ birthday meal for my Grandpa.

12. We all _ a trophy for our performance.

13. Our _ are a complete nightmare.

14. It was a _ day for my family.

15. It was a _ _ _ _ _ _ _ _ _ _ _ _ _ _ _ _ _ _ _ feeling.

16. It was a _ _ _ _ _ _ _ _ _ _ _ _ _ _ _ _ _ _ _ full of historical beauty.

17. The _ to my cupboard would not close.

18. I tried to _ _ _ _ _ _ _ _ _ _ _ _ _ _ _ _ _ _ _ the bully at school.

19. The _ _ _ _ _ _ _ _ _ _ _ _ _ _ _ _ _ _ _ needed to be checked before it was used.

20. I was so _.

KEY STAGE 2
English

SET B
Practice Paper 3
Comprehension

Reading & Comprehension

1 hour

First Name	
Middle Name/s	
Last Name	
School	
Date of Birth	DD / MM / YYYY

BLAZE AND THE
CRYSTAL DIADEM

THE LIFE OF
HENRY VIII

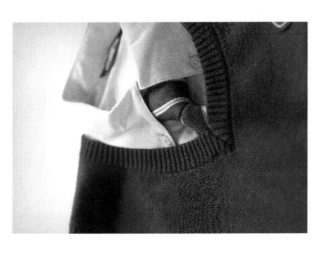

SHOULD SCHOOL
UNIFORMS
BE COMPULSORY?

Read the text carefully and answer the following questions.

Extract from *Blaze and the Crystal Diadem* by How2Become.

If you walked down the street, it became crystal clear that the children all had one thing in common; about 4 inches above their heads floated human silhouettes. These 6 inch tall silhouettes were known as 'The Minders', and every child had one until they reached the age of 16.

The Minders were provided to each child after their first breath, and from that day forward, the child was shielded from all manners of evil. Parents were none the wiser, and assumed their child had an imaginary friend, and in some respect, they were right. Yet, what adults were oblivious to, was the fact that they were real to every child and they were real to the realms from which they came.

The ability to look beyond the realms of the real world, and only see the land in its most pure and naïve manner, allowed children to enter the world of superheroes and grow up feeling sheltered, safe and shielded.

One sudden and unpreventable event occurred on the 25th June, which led to the overturning of this harmonious connection. The realm of The Minders felt the impacts of an earthquake which took place around the world. The realm disconnected itself from Earth the moment it felt the tremors and vibrations. Now, with The Minders' purpose in life being shattered to pieces, there was nothing left for them but utter turmoil and doubt.

100 years on, and the land of the superheroes was in total chaos. Not only did they have to live with the fact that they were unable to protect the child to whom they were assigned, but now had to face the notorious and nasty supervillain, Blaze.

Blaze was uncontrollable; he had killed hundreds of his fellow Minders, and taken to a life of crime and evil: simply *too hot to handle*. He slept on a gold, silk hammock positioned at the peak of a mountain. Blaze was very fond of this spot, for this spot he could experience the first glisten of sunlight every morning. Peering down was the destroyed village; the handy work of The Almighty. From high above, he could overlook everything and everyone. But, what he was unable to see, was the cunning plan to seek resolution and take back the crystal diadem.

The crystal diadem stood on a golden post, right by the side of his hammock. It was guarded by four, frightened fairies, who could not escape the powers of Almighty Blaze.

Down in the enchanted forest, a group of superheroes were huddled together. Nothing more than faint whispers could be heard. They stood contemplating for several minutes, before branching out.

"Everyone know what they are supposed to do?" asked Preston. He stood dressed in a bright uniform, which was as blue as the ocean. His power was knowledge, and he had perfected a plan to get the crystal diadem back. For the diadem possessed all kinds of magic, and gave the holder the utmost power and strength.

"What if it doesn't work," said Lalita, a pretty young girl dressed all in pink. "This is our last chance." Whilst the most afraid, she was the strongest out of her fellow comrades.

Lalita was reassured by Preston, who was optimistic about his plan to save the realm of The Minders and defeat Blaze once and for all.

Once again, they regrouped in a circle: Preston, Lalita, Freddie, Anil and Scarlett. Five lifelong friends who had each minded a child that provided special skills. These skills had all borne superpowers, which represented the only chance of beating the burning Blaze of horror.

As the sun began to fade, the lights of the village became their only guide. Every cold burst of wind was like a bee's sting. The leaves began to shudder and the wind began to whistle. The whole village came to a standstill, and the stillness offered nothing but emptiness and silence.

Hand in hand, the superheroes took one deep breath before ascending rapidly into the air. As each superhero soared, they each yelled out their skills.

Knowledge, strength, invisibility, fire manipulation, telepathy.

Blaze and his domestics were sitting quietly in the mountain's pitch blackness. The only colours to come from the top of the mountain were the bright flames which illuminated from Blaze's evil hands.

The superheroes landed in the points of a pentagon. The dark nothingness allows the superheroes to move about fairly easy without the worry of being caught, for Blaze's power is not reading minds nor immaculate hearing, it is the flaming fireballs that flood from his hands.

Scarlett slowly creeps up behind the gold post which is home to the crystal diadem. *This was* easy, she thought to herself.

Overlooking her, Preston could see her every move. Although he did not have a visual on the whereabouts of Blaze, his expression was of slight concern.

"It shouldn't be this easy!" Preston told himself.

As Scarlett leaned in and grabbed the diadem, the fairies began to squeal. She soared up into the air and started circling the mountain to find the others, only to be stopped by Blaze.

Flames poured from Blaze's hands. His anger made him turn a shade of purple.

"Give me that now, you thief!" demanded Blaze.

"It's not yours, Blaze. We're taking it back to where it belongs," Scarlett said, with fear trembling in her voice.

"Never!" shouted Blaze. He rolled a ball of flames between his hands, smirking at Scarlett. In one flash, the ball of flames shot through the air and hit Scarlett straight in the heart. Her powers were useless and there was nothing she could do. She plummeted to the floor, where she lay stagnant and powerless.

Question 1

What kind of text is this? Circle **one**.

NON-FICTION   PLAY   FICTION   POETRY

Give reasons for your answer.

_____

_____

1 mark

Question 2

"If you walked down the street, it became crystal clear that the children all had one thing in common..."

Which of the following words could the writer have used instead of using 'crystal clear'? Circle **one**.

SPARKLY   PRECIOUS   OBLIVIOUS   EVIDENT

1 mark

Question 3

Write the numbers 1 to 6 in the boxes based on the order in which they happened.

Blaze shoots a fireball at Scarlett.

A group of superheroes were huddled together.

Scarlett grabs the diadem.

The Minders safeguard children under the age of 16.

Blaze and his fairy domestics are sitting quietly.

An earthquake takes place.

1 mark

Question 4

List the **five** superhero powers.

1. _____

2. _____

3. _____

4. _____

5. _____

Question 5

> *"They stood contemplating for several minutes, before branching out."*

What does the word 'contemplating' mean?

_____

_____

_____

_____

Question 6

> *"She plummeted to the floor, where she lay stagnant and powerless."*

What do you think the word 'stagnant' means in this phrase?

_____

_____

_____

_____

Question 7

The writer uses alliterative language to make their writing more descriptive. Rewrite two alliterations and explain the impact this has on the reader.

ALLITERATION 1

_____

_____

ALLITERATION 2

_____

_____

2 marks

Question 8

In the last paragraph, the writer explains how Scarlett's superhero power was useless. Explain why there is a good chance that her superhero power is not fire manipulation. Use **examples** from the text to support your answer.

_____

_____

_____

_____

_____

_____

2 marks

Question 9

Based on your understanding of the text, why do you think Blaze has stolen the crystal diadem?

_____

_____

_____

_____

_____

Question 10

The writer uses a simile. Write out the simile and explain the significance of using this literary technique.

_____

_____

_____

_____

Question 11

"The leaves began to shudder and the wind began to whistle."

What literary technique is this? Circle **one**.

| SIMILE | METAPHOR | HYPERBOLE | IRONY |

Give a definition of the literary technique you have chosen.

_____

_____

Question 12

"Blaze was uncontrollable; he had killed hundreds of his fellow Minders, and taken to a life of crime and evil: *simply too hot to handle.*"

Why do you think the writer has written 'too hot to handle' in italics?

_____

_____

_____

_____

_____

_____

_____

_____

1 mark

Question 13

Create the next three paragraphs for this story. Remember to focus on your grammar, punctuation and spelling. You will be awarded marks for creative thinking and descriptive writing.

_____

_____

_____

_____

_____

_____

_____

_____

_____

3 marks

Read the text carefully and answer the following questions.

The Life of Henry VIII by How2Become.

Henry VIII is one of the most famous and recognisable kings in English history, reigning from 1509 to 1547. He was known for his egotism and ruthlessness. Henry was heartless and cruel to anyone who did not agree with him, and they would often suffer the harshest punishments, including death.

Aside from being selfish, he is mostly talked about still in regards to his six wives. Monarchs during the Tudor times seldom married for love. Instead, they would often marry based on power and wealth.

THE WIVES

Henry VIII married a Spanish princess, Catherine of Aragon, in 1509. They divorced in 1533, and Catherine later died in 1536. She had previously been married to Henry's brother, Arthur. She gave birth to a daughter, Mary, who later became Queen Mary I. Henry's reason for wanting a divorce was the fact that she failed to produce a male heir for him. Their marriage was annulled.

Henry married Anne Boleyn in 1533, in secret. She gave birth to the future Queen Elizabeth I, but, when she suffered a miscarriage in 1536, Henry accused her of witchcraft and sentenced her to death.

Next, Henry married Jane Seymour. This was just eleven days after Henry had sentenced his previous wife to death. Jane gave birth to a boy in 1537, but died 12 days later. Jane was buried at Windsor Castle; the future resting place of Henry himself.

In 1540, Henry married Anne of Cleves. Her nationality was German, and it was thought that their marriage was based on forming a tie between England and the Protestant Princess of Germany. However, Henry found this alliance to his disadvantage and divorced her that very same year.

Henry then married Catherine Howard in 1540, whom he later accused of adultery. He had Catherine beheaded at the Tower of London in 1542.

Finally, Henry married Katherine Parr In 1543. Katherine outlived Henry; so she is said to have 'survived'. Henry died in 1547 and was laid to rest at Windsor Castle.

TIMELINE OF KEY FACTS

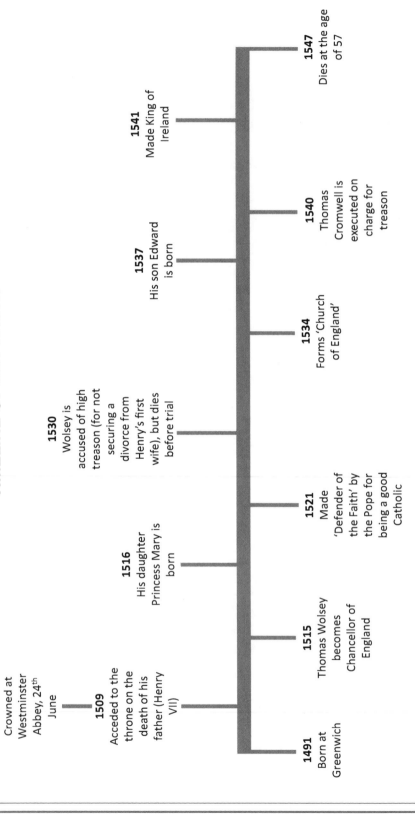

1491
Born at Greenwich

1509
Acceded to the throne on the death of his father (Henry VII)

Crowned at Westminster Abbey, 24th June

1515
Thomas Wolsey becomes Chancellor of England

1516
His daughter Princess Mary is born

1521
Made 'Defender of the Faith' by the Pope for being a good Catholic

1530
Wolsey is accused of high treason (for not securing a divorce from Henry's first wife), but dies before trial

1534
Forms 'Church of England'

1537
His son Edward is born

1540
Thomas Cromwell is executed on charge for treason

1541
Made King of Ireland

1547
Dies at the age of 57

Question 1
What year was Henry VIII born?

_____

Question 2

"He was known for his egotism and ruthlessness."

Which of the following statements best defines the word 'egotism'?
Tick **one**.

Henry VIII was considered an aggressive and hostile man. ☐

Henry VIII was considered a feeble man. ☐

Henry VIII was considered noble and generous man. ☐

Henry VIII was considered to be extremely self-absorbed. ☐

1 mark

Question 3

Freddie loves inferences! Based on the information provided,
which marriage was Henry VIII most fond of? Explain your answer
using **examples** from the text.

_____
_____
_____
_____
_____
_____
_____
_____

2 marks

Question 4

When was Henry the VIII crowned 'King of Ireland'?

_____

Question 5

For the following statements, put a **tick** in the box to show if the statement is **true**, and put a **cross** in the box where the statement in **false**.

STATEMENT	TRUE	FALSE
Henry divorced three of his wives.		
Henry VIII was born in 1491.		
Henry's first child was a daughter called Elizabeth.		
Henry's second marriage was to Anne Boleyn.		
Anne of Cleves's nationality was German.		
Henry's first wife was married to his brother.		

Question 6

When was the Church of England formed?

_____

Question 7

What does the VIII stand for in Henry VIII? Circle **one**.

5   6   7   8   9

Question 8

Lalita needs your help. Help her match the names up with the correct dates in which they were married to Henry VIII.

WIFE

DATES

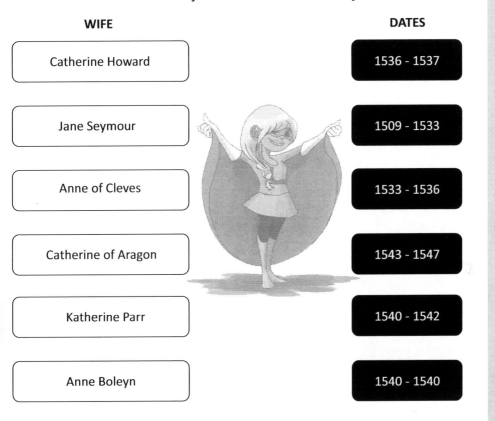

Catherine Howard

1536 - 1537

Jane Seymour

1509 - 1533

Anne of Cleves

1533 - 1536

Catherine of Aragon

1543 - 1547

Katherine Parr

1540 - 1542

Anne Boleyn

1540 - 1540

3 marks

Question 9

Using the information from the text, explain why you think it was important for Henry VIII to have a son.

_____

_____

_____

_____

_____

_____

2 marks

Question 10

Match the names of each of Henry VIII's wives with how their marriage ended.

Catherine of Aragon	Jane Seymour	Katherine Parr	Catherine Howard	Anne Boleyn	Anne of Cleves

SURVIVED	BEHEADED	DIVORCED	BEHEADED	DIED	DIVORCED

2 marks

Read the text carefully and answer the following questions.

Should school uniforms be compulsory? by How2Become.

SHOULD SCHOOL UNIFORMS BE COMPULSORY?

There has been a mammoth amount of debate regarding school uniforms, and whether or not they should be compulsory. Undeniably, there are both benefits and drawbacks to having an established school uniform. See below for the breakdowns.

YES – they should be compulsory

The importance of uniforms signifies unity; it shows a team atmosphere. This allows for every student to feel a sense of acceptance and unison. Certain students will not feel belittled for not wearing high-end fashion items, so common school issues such as bullying will not be as severe. School uniforms allow every student to feel of equal value – school is a place for learning, not a place to flaunt your wealth.

If students were allowed to choose their own clothing, this could consequently detract from their learning. Students, particularly in secondary school, are at a vulnerable age. They are at a time in their life when not only do they have to deal with hormones and changing bodies, but also with exams and good grades. Having one less thing to think about means that they are able to concentrate on the most important aspects of education, as opposed to what trainers they wear or what brands they follow.

School uniforms are also a great way to prepare children for the wider world, as in the future; most lines of work will require them to adhere to a certain dress code.

Of course, freedom of choice is important too, but there is a time and place, and allowing too much choice at such an impressionable age could have long-lasting implications.

NO – they should not be compulsory

We should be encouraging students to express their individuality. Their choice of clothing is a fantastic way to do this, and is a key form of expression. People are unique, and shouldn't be grouped together in a collectivist fashion.

Having a uniform is actually more distracting than not having one. Obeying the rules of school uniform often involves complex rules of formality. For example:

- Shirt buttoned up so far;
- Ties to a certain length;
- Sleeves not rolled up;
- Skirts to a certain length.

All of the aforementioned can detract from students' learning. Allowing children to wear a relaxed and comfortable choice of clothing will have positive effects in the long run.

For generations, school uniforms have been implemented for both practical and social reasons. Practically speaking, school uniforms are worn five times a week, and therefore reduce the worry and money spent on different items of clothes per day.

School uniforms are a great equaliser in regards to social status. It does not matter what background you come from, or who your family is, everyone looks the same in school uniform.

However, the reality of uniforms seems lost on some people, and the rules surrounding uniform seem to be relaxing. If you walk down the street, you are bound to see a boy with rolled up sleeves, tie off and his top button undone. You will see girls wearing short skirts, which are evidently shorter than the guided rules of conduct. What's the point of codes of conduct when they're not abided by one hundred percent?

Are school uniforms fading out?

Question 1

What type of non-fiction text is this? Circle **one**.

INFORMATIVE   PERSUASIVE   DISCUSSION   RECOUNT

Explain how you know this.

_____

_____

_____

_____

1 mark

Question 2

From reading the text, what do 'uniforms' signify?

_____

_____

1 mark

Question 3

Which of the following statements are arguments **for** school uniforms being compulsory. Tick **two**.

Children can express themselves freely. ☐

School uniforms reduce the chances of bullying. ☐

School uniforms last longer than everyday clothes. ☐

School uniforms allow for the school to be branded. ☐

School uniforms provide equality. ☐

2 marks

Question 4

Give another argument why you think school uniforms should be compulsory.

_____

_____

_____

1 mark

Question 5

Give another argument why you think school uniforms should not be compulsory.

_____

_____

_____

1 mark

Question 6

"There has been a mammoth amount of debate regarding school uniforms, and whether or not they should be compulsory."

What do you think the writer means by the term 'mammoth'?

_____

_____

1 mark

Question 7

"Are school uniforms fading out?"

a) What literary technique is this?

_____

1 mark

b) Why do you think the writer has used this as the last line of the text?

_____

_____

_____

1 mark

Question 8

Scarlett is undecided about what side she agrees with.

Which side of the argument do you agree with and why?

Support your answer using **examples** from both the text, and your own **personal** views.

_____

_____

_____

_____

_____

_____

_____

_____

3 marks

Question 9

"Their choice of clothing is a fantastic way to do this, and is a key form of expression."

What do you think the writer means by the term 'expression'?

_____

_____

_____

1 mark

Question 10

"School uniforms allow every student to feel of equal value – it is a place for learning, not a place to flaunt your wealth."

What other word could replace the word 'flaunt'? Circle **one**.

DISPLAY   COVER   FORTUNE   ADMIRE   DEFY

1 mark

Question 11

"People are unique, and shouldn't be grouped together in a collectivist fashion."

What do you think the word 'collectivist' mean?

_____

_____

_____

1 mark

Question 12

Why do you think the writer compares school uniforms with the world of work?

_____

_____

_____

_____

1 mark

KEY STAGE 2
English

SET B
Answer Booklet

Answers to Paper 1, Paper 2 and Paper 3

*Using the answers in this booklet, carefully add up the total marks for each paper. The total marks for each **SET** will be out of 120.*

You can use these marks to monitor your child's progression and work on their weaker areas.

	Paper 1 Mark out of 50	Paper 2 Mark out of 20	Paper 3 Mark out of 50	TOTAL Mark out of 120
SET B				

Answers to Set B

Paper 1

Q1.

a) Julie asked for a <u>piece</u> of cake.

b) My mum went to the bank and had to <u>queue</u> for an hour.

c) <u>They're</u> going to need a bigger boat.

1 mark

Q2. D – "Stop it?" should the teacher.

The question mark should be replaced by an exclamation mark. The teacher is not asking a question, instead it is a command.

1 mark

Q3. Disconnect, **mis**lead, **mis**treat, **mis**understood, **dis**honest, **dis**ability, **dis**loyal, **mis**print

1 mark

Q4.

a) My teacher <u>gave</u> me detention.

b) Lilly <u>was</u> going to Italy during the summer holidays.

c) My dad <u>taught</u> me how to swim.

d) Blaze, <u>who's</u> an evil villain, is planning revenge.

1 mark

Q5. Your answer should look like this:

SENTENCE	VERB	ADVERB	ADJECTIVE
Henry **declared** his love of football.	✔		
Jordan **scoffed** down his gummy bears.	✔		
Joshua came to work every morning **determined** to succeed.			✔
Richard **sang** really loudly.	✔		
Gemma walked around the room **graciously**.		✔	
Katie **always** got to work early.		✔	

Q6. Bought, shook, thought, laid, left, found

1 mark

Q7. Your answer should look like this:

1 mark

Son	**sun**	Flour	**flower**
Meet	**meat**	Whose	**who's**
None	**nun**	Chews	**choose**
Red	**read**	So	**sew**
For	**four**	Blue	**blew**

Q8.

1 mark

a) It is **definitely** the coldest day of the year.

b) The **principal** wanted to talk to the whole school.

c) The argument played on Millie's **conscience**.

Q9.

2 marks

(2 marks for all correct answers. Award 1 mark for no more than two errors).

a) The cat's bed was full of cat hair.

b) The baby's nappy needed to be changed.

c) This wasn't the best idea. My mum's car was wrecked.

d) The horses that belonged to the jockeys.

e) The children's toys, that were at my Auntie's house, were all over her floor.

Q10. *The relative clauses you create can be anything, so long as it fits in with the main clause.*

<u>For example:</u>

a) My father went fishing, but he caught nothing.

b) Rachel was late home from school because she had detention.

c) Leah went to the school disco; she had fun.

d) Charlie and Megan played on the swings, they wanted to go higher and higher.

1 mark

Q11. Your answer should look like this:

1 mark

Sentence	Main Clause	Subordinate Clause
Although I was scared of the water, I jumped in the pool.		✔
My best friend is expecting a baby; I'm happy for her.	✔	
Blaze shoots fire from his hands – **an impressive superpower!**		✔
When the teacher turned her back, **the students would throw paper around.**	✔	

Q12. *You could have created any 3 sentences, so long as you have used the hyphen and the dashes in the correct place.*

Get a parent or teacher to check your answer.

Remember, a hyphen is used to join words that have a close meaning, whereas dashes should be used similarly to brackets.

3 marks

(1 mark for 3 sentences using hyphens correctly, 1 mark for correct use of dashes, and 1 mark for explaining the difference).

Q13.

a) The school choir had **practice** three times a week.

b) I need some **advice** about what to do.

c) I need to **practise** my dance moves.

d) I **advise** you to take your time and think about it very carefully.

e) My brother tries to **practise** his football every day, but sometimes is late to his football **practice**.

1 mark

Q14. Your answer should look like this:

	- Ist	- Ism	- Ery
Art	✔		✔
Tour	✔	✔	
Cook			✔
Real	✔	✔	
Station			✔

1 mark

Q15.

Matt and James like playing hockey.

It was time that I went to bed.

2 marks

(2 marks for both correct answers. Award 1 mark for one correct answer).

Q16. Your answer should look like this:

	ADD –CIAL OR –TIAL	SYLLABLES	NUMBER OF SYLLABLES
Confiden_____	Confidential	Con-fi-den-tial	4
Essen_____	Essential	E-ssen-tial	3
Cru_____	Crucial	Cru-cial	2
Finan_____	Financial	Fi-nan-cial	3
Ini_____	Initial	In-i-tial	3
Par_____	Partial	Par-tial	2

2 marks

(2 marks for all correct answers. Award 1 mark for no more than two errors).

Q17. Su<u>bt</u>le, s<u>c</u>issors, <u>g</u>uide, cas<u>t</u>le, Chris<u>t</u>mas, bisc<u>u</u>it, i<u>s</u>le, <u>h</u>our, w<u>h</u>en, lam<u>b</u>, r<u>h</u>ino, w<u>h</u>ite, <u>w</u>rap, he<u>d</u>ge, <u>g</u>nome

2 marks

(2 marks for all correct answers. Award 1 mark for no more than three errors).

Q18.

1. Only 30 centimetres in height, meerkats depend on group cooperation to survive in the Kalahari Desert. One meerkat will stand up on its hind legs (propped up by its tail) and act as a lookout, while the others look for food.

2. Areas of Outstanding Natural Beauty (AONB) are landscapes that offer beauty and nature and need safeguarding. These AONBs include rocky shores, sand dunes, saltmarshes, sandy beaches, cliffs and many more.

3. During World War II, children were evacuated to protect them from air raids. Children were mainly sent to the countryside, where there were less risks of air raids. These children were taken in by families across the country.

3 marks

(Award 1 mark for each correct passage).

Q19. Your answer should look like this:

ACTIVE VOICE	PASSIVE VOICE
I made a paper aeroplane.	A paper aeroplane was made by me.
Elaine cut the grass.	The grass was cut by Elaine.
The cat scratched the girl.	The girl was scratched by the cat.
Iceland beat England.	England was beaten by Iceland.

1 mark

Q20. Your answer should look like this:

PASSIVE VOICE	ACTIVE VOICE
The kitchen is cleaned by Martin.	Martin cleaned the kitchen.
The customer was being helped by the sales assistant.	The sales assistant helped the customer.
The car was stolen by Jim.	Jim stole the car.
The bike was repaired by Damien.	Damien repaired the bike.

1 mark

Q21. *You can add any alliteration so long as it fits in with the rest of the sentence.*

1 mark

For example:

a) The **buzzing** bees were hovering around the park.

b) The **enchanted** elves were dressed in **colourful** clothes.

c) We watched the **sparkling** stars using a **tiny** telescope.

d) We got to touch the **enormous** elephant. It was **absolutely** amazing.

Q22.

1 mark

1. It **might** be possible
   POSSIBILITY
2. **Should** I do my homework?
   POSSIBILITY
3. It **will be** cold tomorrow.
   CERTAINTY
4. Yasmin **can** play the piano.
   CERTAINTY

Q23. 1. The birds <u>flew</u> gracefully in the sky. 2. The glass table, which was <u>made</u> by Sam's neighbour, was <u>smashed</u> to pieces. 3. Blaze <u>jumped</u> from rooftop to rooftop. He <u>searched</u> for the superheroes, who he was <u>trying</u> to <u>defeat</u>. 4. I <u>laughed</u> and <u>smiled</u> a lot. My best friend <u>makes</u> me <u>feel</u> incredibly <u>happy</u>.	**1 mark**
Q24. *You could have created any sentence you want, so long as you have used the conjunction in the correct place.* For example: Sam likes neither Brussel sprouts **nor** parsnips. I love every flavour ice cream **except** strawberry. My parents went on holiday **but** I decided to stay with my grandparents. He was my best friend **despite** all our arguments.	**1 mark**
Q25. a) If you use the word **ITS**, you are showing that something belongs to someone or something. **TRUE** b) Names ending in 'S' will only need an apostrophe when demonstrating possession. **FALSE – you will need to use an apostrophe and another 'S'. E.g. Rhys's watch.** c) The following sentence uses the apostrophe correctly: "My neighbours' cars are always parked outside my house." **TRUE**	**1 mark**

Q26.

a) "We need to get a move on," said Harry.

b) Rob asked, "Can I stay outside and play for 10 more minutes?"

c) The report said: "The school encouraged children's learning in a fun and unique way."

d) "I was terrified! I didn't know what to do!" said a young, frightened boy.

2 marks

(2 marks for all correct answers. Award 1 mark for no more than two errors).

Q27. Formal writing is writing used for professional or academic purposes. It uses technical, well-spoken language and a professional tone. Informal language is more 'casual' and often uses abbreviations or slang.

EXAMPLE 1

Informal language in the style of a diary entry

EXAMPLE 2

Formal language in the style of a letter addressed to an organisation or professional.

3 marks

(1 mark for correct explanation.
1 mark for example of informal writing.
1 mark for formal writing example).

Q28.

ADJECTIVES = energetic, sequinned

NOUNS = Vincent/Salsa/dance/shirt

1 mark

Q29. *These commands and exclamations can be anything so long as you demonstrate them correctly.*

For example

COMMAND 1 = Come here now!

COMMAND 2 = Pick up your rubbish!

EXCLAMATION 1 = What a good friend you are!

EXCLAMATION 2 = I cannot find my rucksack!

2 marks

(2 marks for all correct sentences. Award 1 mark for two correct sentences).

Q30. Your answer should look like this: **2 marks**

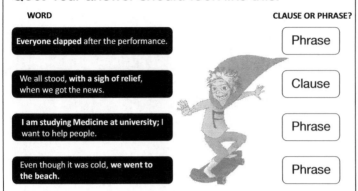

WORD   CLAUSE OR PHRASE?

Everyone clapped after the performance.	Phrase
We all stood, **with a sigh of relief,** when we got the news.	Clause
I am studying Medicine at university; I want to help people.	Phrase
Even though it was cold, **we went to the beach.**	Phrase

Q31.

The baby was crying because she had two teeth coming through.

This country was known for having many volcanoes.

2 marks

(1 mark for each correct box ticked).

Q32.

Circled = "As quick as a flash"

Underlined = "elegantly", "powerfully"

1 mark

Q33. My friends from school, all of whom I am still in contact with, have arranged a party before everyone leaves for university.

1 mark

Q34. Your answer should look like this: **2 marks**

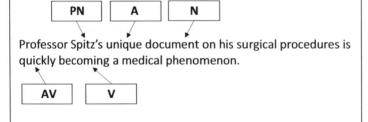

Professor Spitz's unique document on his surgical procedures is quickly becoming a medical phenomenon.

PN   A   N

AV   V

(2 marks for all correct labels. Award 1 mark for no more than two errors).

Q35. *You could have chosen any synonym.*	**1 mark**
<u>For example:</u> Exhausted, drowsy, sleepy, worn out, drained, fatigued, enervated *There are lots of other synonyms, so get a teacher or parent to look at your word if it's not listed above.*	

Paper 2

Spelling 1 = argument

Spelling 2 = February

Spelling 3 = believe

Spelling 4 = beautiful

Spelling 5 = because

Spelling 6 = interesting

Spelling 7 = their

Spelling 8 = our

Spelling 9 = thought

Spelling 10 = different

Spelling 11 = surprise

Spelling 12 = received

Spelling 13 = neighbours

Spelling 14 = special

Spelling 15 = peculiar

Spelling 16 = country

Spelling 17 = drawer

Spelling 18 = avoid

Spelling 19 = parachute

Spelling 20 = embarrassed

Paper 3

[Blaze and the Crystal Diadem]

Q1. Fiction This is based on a made up story, which uses fantasy and imagination to demonstrate creative writing.	**1 mark**
Q2. Evident	**1 mark**
Q3. Your answer should look like this:	**1 mark**

Blaze shoots a fireball at Scarlett.	6
A group of superheroes were huddled together.	3
Scarlett grabs the diadem.	5
The Minders safeguard children under the age of 16.	1
Blaze and his fairy domestics are sitting quietly.	4
An earthquake takes place.	2

Q4. Knowledge, strength, invisibility, fire manipulation, telepathy	**1 mark**
Q5. The word contemplating means to consider something carefully. The superheroes are creating a plan to get the crystal diadem.	**1 mark**
Q6. The word stagnant in this phrase is used to show that Scarlett is not moving. She has been hit by a fireball and is now unable to fight back.	**1 mark**

Q7.

ALLITERATION 1 = "crystal clear"

The writer uses this alliteration to emphasise the point that it should be quite obvious.

ALLITERATION 2 = "flaming fireballs"

This alliteration provides the reader with not only more description, but also emphasises power.

2 marks

(1 mark for each alliteration and explanation).

Q8. You could suggest that if Scarlett's superhero power had been fire and heat manipulation, she would not have been struck down. Instead, she would have been able to control and manipulate the heat in order to protect herself. In the passage, the writer claims that "her powers were useless and there was nothing she could do". This suggests that her superhero power was unable to prevent this from happening.

2 marks

(1 mark for a reasonable suggestion, and 1 mark for using examples from the text).

Q9. One possible reason could be that Blaze has stolen the diadem to control everyone else in his realm. The fact that the crystal diadem possesses strong powers means that Blaze wants control and the power that comes with it. The fact that the superheroes are trying to defeat Blaze suggests that Blaze is going to destroy the realm, in some way or another.

2 marks

(1 mark for a reasonable suggestion, and 1 mark for using examples from the text).

Q10. "Every cold burst of wind was like a bee's sting".

The writer uses this simile to suggest that the wind was bitter cold and was stinging. This not only creates visual imagery, but allows the reader to get a sense of the change in weather, as the battle commences between the superheroes and Blaze.

1 mark

Q11. Metaphor A metaphor is used to describe objects using nouns or verbs that do not *literally* make sense, but paint a certain picture when used *figuratively*. In this case, leaves do not *literally* shudder like people do, but the word '*shudder*' creates an eerie image of the setting.	**1 mark**
Q12. You could say how this phrase is written in italics because it emphasises the key characteristics of Blaze's superpowers. It could also suggest that this is his catchphrase, and that he is simply '*too hot to handle*'.	**1 mark**
Q13. *Your paragraphs can be anything you want to be, so long as it ties in with the overall tone and theme of the narrative.* *This question will focus on your grammar, punctuation and spelling, as well as your ability to think creatively.* *Get a parent or teacher to look at your paragraphs, and assess you based on the aforementioned.*	**3 marks** (Marks to be awarded for good use of grammar, punctuation and spelling. This question also assesses your creative ability).

Q1. 1491

1 mark

Q2. Henry VIII was considered to be extremely self-absorbed.

1 mark

Q3. Based on the information provided, Henry VIII was most fond of Jane Seymour. Jane Seymour was buried at Windsor Castle, the same resting place as Henry VIII himself. This could suggest that he loved her more. She also was the only wife to provide him with a son, which is what he wanted.

2 marks

Q4. 1541

1 mark

Q5. Your answer should look like this:

2 marks

STATEMENT	TRUE	FALSE
Henry divorced three of his wives.		✘
Henry VIII was born in 1491.	✔	
Henry's first child was a daughter called Elizabeth.		✘
Henry's second marriage was to Anne Boleyn.	✔	
Anne of Cleves's nationality was German.	✔	
Henry's first wife was married to his brother.	✔	

(Award 2 marks for all correct answers. Award 1 mark for no more than two errors).

Q6. 1534

1 mark

Q7. 8

1 mark

Q8. Your answer should look like this:

WIFE	DATES
Catherine Howard	1536 - 1537
Jane Seymour	1509 - 1533
Anne of Cleves	1533 - 1536
Catherine of Aragon	1543 - 1547
Katherine Parr	1540 - 1542
Anne Boleyn	1540 - 1540

3 marks

(3 marks for all correct answers. 2 marks for no more than two errors. 1 mark for more than two errors).

Q9. It was important for Henry VIII to secure a male heir to continue the royal line, as having a son as your heir was considered much more favourable than a daughter in those times.

Henry wanted his son to become king and take over his responsibilities when the time came.

2 marks

(2 marks for a reasonable suggestion, using information from the passage to support answer).

Q10. Your answer should look like this:

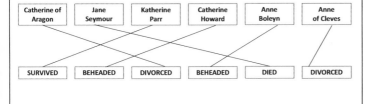

2 marks

(2 marks for all correct answers. Award 1 mark for no more than two errors).

Q1. Discussion This non-fiction piece of writing is a discussion text. It uses two alternative views to debate the same subject. It uses arguments for and against an issue, and uses emotive language in order to appeal to its reader.	**1 mark**
Q2. Uniforms signify equality and harmony. With everyone dressed the same, it allows for each student to be represented as being part of a team, as opposed to individuals.	**1 mark**
Q3. School uniforms can reduce the chances of bullying. School uniforms provide equality.	**2 marks** (Award 1 mark for each sentence).
Q4. *You can come up with any argument you want, so long as it's **for** school uniforms being compulsory.* <u>For example:</u> School uniforms allow for schools to be recognisable outside the school grounds. If children walked around in their own clothes, the public would have trouble determining what school they belong to, and whether they are students.	**1 mark**

Q5. *You can come up with any argument you want, so long as it's **against** school uniforms being compulsory.* For example: School uniforms are teaching students to mature beyond their age. In primary school, students are made to adhere to strict rules. Children should be able to act their age, as opposed to conforming to the norms of the outside world. School uniforms are made from one material, which may irritate some children. Therefore, children should be able to feel comfortable during their school hours.	**1 mark**
Q6. The word mammoth is used in this sentence to emphasise enormous amounts of debate.	**1 mark**
Q7. a) Rhetorical question b) The writer uses this literary technique in order to get the readers to question this topic themselves. It draws the reader in and makes the text interactive.	**1 mark** **1 mark**
Q8. *This is based on personal response. Make sure you use examples from the text, as well as your own personal opinions.*	**3 marks**
Q9. The term 'expression' means the ability to express oneself.	**1 mark**
Q10. Display	**1 mark**

Q11. The term collectivist means that students wearing uniforms are grouped together collectively, with no individual characteristics.

1 mark

Q12. School uniforms are compared with the world of work, to show that people are conforming to the rules and codes of conducts that are set out for them. In schools, children must obey a dress code. In the world of work, employees also have to adhere to the codes of conduct regarding wardrobe.

1 mark

[END OF SET B]

KEY STAGE 2
English

External Use

APPENDICES
Set A and Set B
Spelling Papers

NOT TO BE VIEWED BY THE TEST TAKER

These appendices are to be used in conjunction with the Spelling papers. These appendices should not be viewed by the test taker, and should be used by a parent/guardian, teacher, or anyone helping their child during their practice questions.

For the purpose of this section, a person (NOT the test taker) will need to:

- Read out the word that the child needs to spell;
- Next, read out an example sentence containing that word;
- The word will then be repeated.

SPELLING

Appendix A needs to be used in conjunction with
SET A Paper 2 (Spelling).

For this paper, you will require the assistance of someone else. If you haven't passed the book over to someone else, please do so now!

How to work through the paper:

The child will have to complete sentences and fill in the correct spelling of the word that is read out to them.

As the assistant, you will need to read the following, and allow the child to write the correct spelling down.

SPELLING 1

The word is **advice**.

*My best friend offered her **advice**.*

The word is **advice**.

SPELLING 2

The word is **aware**

*I was not **aware** of the circumstances.*

The word is **aware**.

SPELLING 3

The word is **suitable**.

*I had to find some clothes that were **suitable** for a wedding.*

The word is **suitable**.

SPELLING 4

The word is **definite**.

*Our plans to go away for the weekend were not **definite**.*

The word is **definite**.

SPELLING 5

The word is **pronunciation**.

*I was asked to work on my **pronunciation**.*

The word is **pronunciation**.

SPELLING 6

The word is **profession**.

*My father's **profession** was being a dentist.*

The word is **profession**.

SPELLING 7

The word is **sufficient**.

*There was not **sufficient** evidence to convict the suspect.*

The word is **sufficient**.

SPELLING 8

The word is **mischievous**.

*The **mischievous** boy was sent out of the classroom for bad behaviour.*

The word is **mischievous**.

SPELLING 9

The word is **honour**.

*It would be an **honour** to meet the Queen.*

The word is **honour**.

SPELLING 10

The word is **scent**.

*The **scent** of the perfume was flowery.*

The word is **scent**.

SPELLING 11

The word is **ridiculed**.

*I was **ridiculed** for wearing trousers that were too big for me.*

The word is **ridiculed**.

SPELLING 12

The word is **pretentious**.

*He was a **pretentious**, old man.*

The word is **pretentious**.

SPELLING 13

The word is **criticised**.

*I was **criticised** for my handwriting.*

The word is **criticised**.

SPELLING 14

The word is **vehicle**.

*My dad's **vehicle** was stolen.*

The word is **vehicle**.

SPELLING 15

The word is **sincere**.

*The young girl sounded **sincere**.*

The word is **sincere**.

SPELLING 16

The word is **disastrous**.

*It turned out to be a **disastrous** trip.*

The word is **disastrous**.

SPELLING 17

The word is **exaggerating**.

*My mum told me off for **exaggerating**.*

The word is **exaggerating**.

SPELLING 18

The word is **environment**.

*For my geography lesson, we looked at the **environment**.*

The word is **environment**.

SPELLING 19

The word is **queue**.

*I had to stand and **queue** for a long time.*

The word is **queue**.

SPELLING 20

The word is **separated**.

*Two of the boys had to be **separated** because they were fighting.*

The word is **separated**.

APPENDIX B

SPELLING

Appendix B needs to be used in conjunction with
SET B Paper 2 (Spelling).

For this paper, you will require the assistance of someone else. If you haven't passed the book over to someone else, please do so now!

<u>How to work through the paper:</u>

The child will have to complete sentences and fill in the correct spelling of the word that is read out to them.

As the assistant, you will need to read the following, and allow the child to write the correct spelling down.

SPELLING 1

The word is **argument**.

*My mum and dad were having an **argument**.*

The word is **argument**.

SPELLING 2

The word is **February**.

*My best friend's birthday is in **February**.*

The word is **February**.

SPELLING 3

The word is **believe**.

*I **believe** that everything happens for a reason.*

The word is **believe**.

SPELLING 4

The word is **beautiful**.

*It was a **beautiful** Monday morning.*

The word is **beautiful**.

SPELLING 5

The word is **because**.

*I got into trouble **because** I was not listening.*

The word is **because**.

SPELLING 6

The word is **interesting**.

*My History lessons were the most **interesting**.*

The word is **interesting**.

SPELLING 7

The word is **their**.

*It was **their** responsibility.*

The word is **their**.

SPELLING 8

The word is **our**.

*The room in **our** house was big and empty.*

The word is **our**.

SPELLING 9

The word is **thought**.

*The **thought** of going to school was unbearable.*

The word is **thought**.

SPELLING 10

The word is **different**.

*My brother and I are extremely **different**.*

The word is **different**.

SPELLING 11

The word is **surprise**.

*We planned a **surprise** birthday meal for my Grandpa.*

The word is **surprise**.

SPELLING 12

The word is **received**.

*We all **received** a trophy for our performance.*

The word is **received**.

SPELLING 13

The word is **neighbours**.

*Our **neighbours** are a complete nightmare.*

The word is **neighbours**.

SPELLING 14

The word is **special**.

*It was a **special** day for my family.*

The word is **special**.

SPELLING 15

The word is **peculiar**.

*It was a **peculiar** feeling.*

The word is **peculiar**.

SPELLING 16

The word is **country**.

*It was a **country** full of historical beauty.*

The word is **country**.

SPELLING 17

The word is **drawer**.

*The **drawer** to my cupboard would not close.*

The word is **drawer**.

SPELLING 18

The word is **avoid**.

*I tried to **avoid** the bully at school.*

The word is **avoid**.

SPELLING 19

The word is **parachute**.

*The **parachute** needed to be checked before it was used.*

The word is **parachute**.

SPELLING 20

The word is **embarrassed**.

*I was so **embarrassed**.*

The word is **embarrassed**.

WANT MORE ENGLISH PRACTICE QUESTIONS?

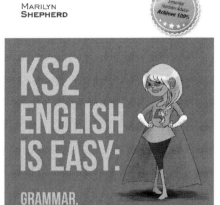

How2Become has created two other FANTASTIC guides to help you and your child prepare for their Key Stage Two (KS2) English SATs.

These exciting guides are filled with fun and interesting facts for your child to engage with to ensure that their revision is fun, and their learning is improved! Invest in your child's future today!

FOR MORE INFORMATION ON OUR KEY STAGE 2 (KS2) GUIDES, PLEASE CHECK OUT THE FOLLOWING:

WWW.HOW2BECOME.COM

WHY NOT TAKE A LOOK AT OUR KS2 MATHS GUIDES!

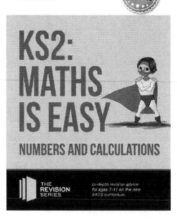

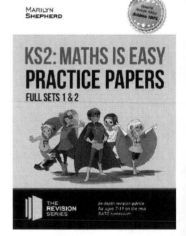

Get Access To
FREE
Psychometric
Tests

www.PsychometricTestsOnline.co.uk

Printed in Great Britain
by Amazon